# IS GOD REAL?

# REAL?

## *PROVE IT!*

A Child's Defense

Pam Antoun

# Endorsements

"*Is God Real? Prove It!* tackles tough questions in a compelling, entertaining story. Highly recommend this book for people who are searching for God and also for young people learning to defend their Christian faith."

—Pastor Jimmy Allen, Lead Pastor, Woodbine Church, Pace, Florida

"Entertaining and fact filled. I love how this book combines apologetics into a fun story."

—Eric Hovind, President and Founder of Pensacola-based organization, Creation Today

"MUST READ if you want your children grounded in the TRUTH that God is real. Perfect for older children and youth, it will help them develop their thinking and equip them for the challenges ahead! The Bible says the truth will set you free! And this book presents the TRUTH for our future generations!"

—Brenda Lewis, Executive Minister, Woodbine Church, Pace, Florida

"Spot on for the Christian community. Proverbs 22:6 clearly instructs, 'train up a child in the way he should go: and when he is old, he will not depart from it.' Conservative figures indicate 70% of our young adults leave the faith after graduation from high school. *Is God Real? Prove*

*It!* helps provide teachers, parents, and children the push back needed to develop and maintain a Biblical word view in their lives. Children are our most valued earthly treasure. Let's pray God will use this book to grow a new generation of apologists for His glory."

—Frank Lay, Principal, LEAD Academy, Pace, Florida

"Powerful, well written, and answers tough questions that often face our children when they are called to defend their faith. I highly recommend this book. I wish I had this book for my two daughters when they were growing up."

—Michelle Medlock Adams, Award winning, best-selling Author

"A brilliant testament to God's existence and wonder, investigated by youth. The author succeeded in guiding those with questions about God and equipping youth to defend their faith in a child's context. This book can be absorbed in one sitting with eternal benefits."

—Ruth "Bootsie" Campbell, Executive Director, Time to Shine Center for Performing Arts, Pace, Florida

"Whether you are an adult or a child, no one is satisfied with the answer 'because I said so.' Our faith is stronger when we can verbalize the reasons why we believe in God, and our witness is more effective when we can give a logical explanation for our beliefs to others. This book helps readers, of any age, explore how to clearly explain their faith to others."

—Alice H. Murray, Esq., Adoption Attorney, Shalimar, Florida

"Well-researched story showing kids talking to kids about their faith. Pam Antoun uses common questions unbelievers ask and answers them in a simple, biblically-based way that is easy to understand. Although this book is written for middle grade children, adults can benefit from it too. I highly recommend this book for youth leaders to show kids how to share and defend their faith."

—Marilyn Turk, Award-winning Christian Author

"*Is God Real? Prove It!* provides children with resources they need to defend their faith. When a classmate approached the author's child because she was a Christian, it was hard for her to put into words why she believed God was real, even though she felt God in her heart. This book helps a Christian child respond with bold, respectful assertiveness."

—Susan Neal, Award-winning Author

"The beauty of Christianity is that children can grasp and understand it. *Is God Real? Prove It!* does a great job showing young people they can help their peers know and understand Christ. This work will be a springboard for many kids starting their faith journey."

—Sam Soutullo, Youth Minister, Woodbine Church, Pace, Florida

"*Is God Real? Prove It!* explains God being real in such a manner that young people will know they have the right answer."

—Sharon Glass, Author

"Equips children and middle-grade youth with the Scriptural truths to stand firm on their faith when questioned "Is God Real?". This is a must buy for parents, churches and children's ministers with the simple story format and review questions for teaching."

—Ann M. Thames, Children's Minister, Woodbine Church, Pace, Florida

"In answer to her own child's questions the author wrote *Is God Real? Prove It!* specifically to prepare children to know God and share their faith in a natural setting. Pam Antoun's love for God and children shines through the text."

—Ellen Earles, Elementary Grade Sunday School Teacher

"I'm excited to have this book in my tool box when explaining to children how to talk about God."

—Michele Marcantonio, Sunday School Teacher and Director of Children of Woodbine Preschool, Pace Florida

But make sure that in your hearts you honor Christ as Lord. Always be ready to give an answer to anyone who asks you about the hope you have. Be ready to give the reason for it. But do it gently and with respect.

—1 Peter 3:15 (NIrV)

# Letter to the Reader

Dear Reader/Friend,

On the playground, a classmate confronted my daughter because she was a Christian. She asked, "How do you know God is real?"

Stumped for words, my daughter said, "It's a feeling in my heart."

That afternoon, my daughter asked me the same question.

I paused to recover from the shock of being asked this from a child. "Wow, that's a fantastic question, honey." Unprepared, I answered, "I know God is real because I can feel His love." After I and many others struggled to answer this question, God led me to write this book to help children provide a convincing response. I pray this book increases your confidence in defending your faith in God and helps everyone who struggles with questions about God.

God created us to know Him and freely choose to love Him. You are God's masterpiece. God created you unique from everyone else so your qualities, experiences, and dreams can all work together to make you an instrument of His love in your own special way. He loves you despite any bad choices you've made.

I pray you choose to love God and accept His gift, Jesus, so nothing will separate you from God's love. I wish you all the best in your journey to know and understand Him.

Much love,
*Pam Antoun*

# Acknowledgments

Thank you to:

- My husband, Amin, and my daughters, Amanda and Jenna, for being unconditionally supportive and encouraging throughout the development of this book.
- Amanda for seeking answers to hard questions about God.
- My writing buddies, reviewers, and instructors for your time, encouragement, and advice: Lydia, Jennifer, Jimmy, Sharon, Ann, Eric, Brittany, Mike, Nan, Ellen, Christine, Susan, Jack, Cece, Jim, Connie, Eva, Susan, Marilyn, Jesse, Cyle, Suzy, Michele, Eve, Beth, Brenda, Ruth, Rita, Michelle, Frank, Alice, Jennifer, Alicia, Terry, Linda, Steph, Rick, Joan, and Josh.
- Those who shared their testimony with me and nurtured me in my spiritual growth.
- My pastor, Jimmy, for answering many questions about God and the Bible.
- My Mother-In-Love, Suzy, for her encouragement and relentless faith that God will bring everything together for completion of this book.
- Everyone who prayed over the development of this book.
- Westbow staff who helped edit, illustrate, coordinate, and publish this book.
- God for your unconditional love, your patience with me, and your desire to have an eternal, loving relationship with everyone.

# Contents

# Why Do You Think God Is Real?

Remember the former things, those of long ago;
I am God, and there is no other;
I am God, and there is none like me.
I make known the end from the beginning,
from ancient times, what is still to come.
I say, "My purpose will stand,
and I will do all that I please."

—Isaiah 46:9–10 (NIV)

**A**fter Amanda's disturbing interaction with the new kid on the bus, weights on her shoulders multiplied, and her eyes grew heavy. She wondered, *How can I defend my belief in You, God? I know You're real, but I don't know how to prove it. I'm just a kid. Please help me.*

Mr. Seymour wrote a homework assignment on the board: "Projects are due in three weeks. Remember …"

Amanda reflected as she tapped her pencil on the desk. She glanced out the classroom window and admired streams of sunrays among dancing yellow and orange leaves. Her gaze landed on the playground, and she dreamed of ways to avoid the new kid after lunch. *I got it,* she thought. *Armed with my sketchbook, I'll sit on the bench and focus completely on drawing. I'm done getting embarrassed.* Her rumbling stomach screamed lunchtime to the class. A red flush filled her face while she sank in her chair.

Mr. Seymour glanced at his watch. "All right, class. Let's line up."

The cafeteria food eased the hunger pains in her stomach. When another student opened the outside door, a gentle breeze swept Amanda's hair from her face and lifted her spirit. The piercing noise in the cafeteria faded as she limped to the bench under the tree. *Finally I'm getting the hang of this crutch,* she thought. The weight on her shoulders lifted as she settled in a comfortable spot and drew.

The rustling of the leaves was replaced with, "Last one to the slide is it."

Amanda cringed. *That voice from the bus.* She lifted her sketchbook like a shield to avoid being noticed.

"On your mark, get set, banana. On your mark, get set, cookie," joked Sophia.

"Hurry up. Let's go." Gavin stumbled over Josiah.

Amanda's toes curled. She shifted her focus to drawing the hill in the opposite direction.

"Go!" Sophia darted to the slide.

Like lightning, Josiah reached the slide first.

Sophia almost reached the slide when… thump. Sophia

slipped on a wet pile of leaves and smacked the ground with her stomach.

Gavin reached the slide second with a huge grin. "You're it, Sophia."

Sophia looked down and brushed the dirt off her shirt. Josiah extended his hand to help her, but she shrugged off his offer. "I'm all right," she said. "I can get up myself."

"Hi, Amanda. Are you going to our **church** fall festival this weekend?" asked Josiah.

Amanda's face lit up at the thought Josiah, one of her neighbors, also went to church. Relief calmed her dread of facing the new anti-God boy again. "Yes, I can't wait."

> **C h u r c h** — *A gathering of people united to learn about and worship God. They are God's hands and feet in loving others.*

A pink blob of gum grew from Sophia's mouth and exploded. "You both go to church?"

*Oh no,* Amanda thought. *Is Sophia antichurch, too? At least she's nice. I wish I could answer the hard questions in class like she does.* She forced a smile toward Josiah.

"Yes, we go to the same church." Josiah leaned closer to Sophia. "Do you want to come to church with us?"

Gavin placed his hands on his hips. "You're kidding. Not you too, Josiah. My dad said church is a building where people get beat up with a **Bible** and loaded with guilt for not being **perfect**."

> **Bible**—The collection of holy writings inspired by God.

Josiah stepped back. "Oh, no, it's not like that. Church is where we learn about God. Did you know God loves you and doesn't want to hurt you? He wants a **relationship** with every person."

> **Perfect**—Without flaw or defect.

The breeze shifted Sophia's pink blob to the side of her face and

> **Relationship**—The way two or more beings deal with each other.

smacked her cheek with a pop. "I've never been to church. What makes you believe God is real?"

Amanda thought about her run-in with Gavin earlier. *There's got to be something I can say besides "I can feel God's love."* Singing bluebirds filled the silence. She glanced at the beauty God created around her. The breeze swayed tall trees. The sun's warmth soothed her cheeks. Patches of yellow and purple flowers dotted the nearby hill. Flocks of birds flew together below fluffy clouds, soft and amazing as cotton candy. "I believe God is real because only God can create something like this from nothing." *Thanks, God,* she said to herself with a sigh of relief.

Goosebumps perked up on Amanda's arms from the shock of her own words.

# Chapter 1 Questions

- - - - - - - - - - - - - - - - - - - - - - - - - - - - - - - - - - - - - - - - -

1. Gavin doesn't go to church because _____

   _____

   _____

   _____.

   What do you think of that?

   _____

   _____

   _____

   _____

   _____

   _____

   _____

2. Amanda believes God is real because only God can create _____ from _____.

3. Is it difficult for you to admit you do or do not go to church? Why or why not?

   _____

   _____

   _____

   _____

   _____

   _____

   _____

# How Can You Create Something from Nothing?

In the beginning God created heaven and earth.
—Genesis 1:1 (NIrV)

**G** avin slipped a toy spider out of his pocket and whispered in Sophia's ear, "Hey, Sophia, you have something crawling on your shoulder."

Sophia flinched. Her hands flew to her shoulders. "There's nothing on my shoulders, goofball." She punched his arm.

Gavin's thin mouth stretched into a slow grin. "Maybe not yet, but I can make something appear on your shoulder." He reached to Sophia's shoulder and grabbed the hairy brown spider off her ear and presented it to her in his hand.

Screams pierced Gavin's ears like a trophy, and Sophia scrunched her face. She leaped back and brushed every imaginary creature off her body at least twice.

Gavin fell to the ground, laughing.

"It's not real." Josiah doubled over, laughing.

"That's disgusting. What a sick joke." Sophia glared at them, hands on her hips.

Gavin screeched with laughter. "Even though it's a toy spider, it's cool that I made it appear on your shoulder."

Amused, Amanda challenged Gavin. "You didn't make that spider. I bet you pulled that spider out of your pocket. Only God can make something from nothing."

Josiah beamed and begged him, "Please show me that trick."

Gavin opened and closed his hands, boasting, "Look, there's nothing in my hands. Now check your ears."

Amanda rubbed her ears. "Nothing there."

"It crawled onto your hair." Gavin grabbed the hideous spider from her hair and proudly revealed it to her.

Amanda snatched the toy spider from Gavin and dangled it high out of his reach. "Now make the spider appear starting with nothing."

"Give it back." Gavin jumped as high as he could, trying to grab his spider from her.

"What's the problem, Gavin? You can't make something from nothing?" She dangled the spider even higher. "Do you agree only God can make something from nothing?"

"Yes! Now give it back! You do have to admit my trick is

pretty cool, though," said Gavin. At last, she lowered the toy spider, reuniting Gavin with his treasured toy.

Sophia tilted her head and crossed her arms. "Amanda, how can you prove God is the One Who created our world?"

Amanda leaned toward Sophia and said, "God tells us about creation in the Bible, and the Bible is proven **trustworthy**."

They headed for the swings.

> **Trustworthy**—Believable.

---

### *** **Did You Know?** ***

"The God-inspired book called the Bible was written during a 1500-year span through more than 40 generations by more than 40 different authors from every walk of life—shepherds, soldiers, prophets, poets, monarchs, scholars, statesmen, masters, servants, tax collectors, fishermen, and tentmakers. Its God-breathed words were written in a variety of places: the wilderness, in a palace, in a dungeon, on a hillside, in a prison, and in exile. It was penned on the continents of Asia, Africa, and Europe and was written in three languages: Hebrew, Aramaic, and Greek. It tells hundreds of stories, records hundreds of songs, and addresses hundreds of controversial subjects. Yet with all its variety of authors, origins, and content, it achieves a miraculous continuity of theme— God's **redemption** of His children and the restoration of all things to His original design." (***The Unshakable Truth***, <u>www. harvesthousepublishers.com</u>)

---

**Redemption**—The act of saving people from sin or evil.

---

# **Chapter 2 Questions**

- - - - - - - - - - - - - - - - - - - - - - - - - - - - - - - - - - - - - - - -

1. God tells us how the world was created in the _____.

2. Do you struggle to defend what you believe about creation? If so, how? _____

_____

_____

_____

_____

_____

_____

_____

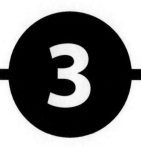

# Why Trust the Bible?

Heaven and earth will pass away, but My
words will by no means pass away.

—Matthew 24:35 (NKJV)

"**A**manda, do you believe everything you read?" Gavin rolled his eyes. "I could write a book, call it the Bible, and say someone created our world. Would you believe that too?"

She smiled. "The Bible isn't just another book. God inspired the writing of the Bible and protected it."

Sophia popped a bubble. "How do you know the Bible came from God?"

Amanda answered, "God gave us a bunch of clues to show us the Bible came from Him. He predicted many events in history before they happened and included them in the Bible."

Gavin said, "I've predicted the weather would be sunny over the weekend, and it was. That doesn't make me God."

Josiah smiled and tilted his head back. "But only God, who knows everything, can *always* accurately predict events before they happen. The Bible contains hundreds of these predictions, called **prophecies**."

Gavin crossed his arms over his chest. "Come on. That's just a number you made up."

> **\* Did You Know? \***
>
> The **Bible** is the most accurate and trustworthy **literature** in history. Literature is a written work that has lasting value.

> **Prophecies—**Telling about events that are going to happen before they occur. God placed prophecies throughout the Bible to show us He inspired the writing of the Bible. The Bible describes hundreds of prophecies, and many have already come true.

"I'm not making it up," said Josiah.

Gavin placed his hands on his hips. "Show me."

Amanda's mouth dropped. "What do you mean? Do you want us to jump in a time machine to repeat history for you?"

Gavin rubbed his chin. "No, but can you give examples of prophecies in the Bible that came true?"

"I don't have the Bible memorized." Amanda stepped backward and silently prayed, *God, how can I help him?*

Gavin looked at Josiah.

"I don't know either," said Josiah. "Maybe we could research it or talk to someone at our church and get you examples."

"Sure you can," Gavin said, smirking.

---

**Prophecy Example 1:**

A **prophet** said Israel's Messiah (a king expected to save them) would be born in the town Bethlehem. Jesus fulfilled this prophecy many years later when He was born in Bethlehem.

---

**Prophecy Example 2:**

Two different prophets predicted how the Messiah would be killed, hundreds of years before crucifixion was even performed. Jesus fulfilled this prophecy and many other prophecies in the Bible.

---

Amanda continued, "Another reason I trust the Bible is it contains many scientific facts which are proven but were not known when the Bible was written. Only God could know those things back then."

Gavin's eyes widened and he said, "Impossible."

Amanda said, "Here's an example. People used to think earth was flat, but the Bible says earth is round."

Gavin said, "That's just a coincidence."

Josiah stood up on a

**\*\*\* Did You Know? \*\*\***

The Bible contains over a hundred scientific facts that were not known during the time the Bible was written. Examples include the earth is round, the ocean contains springs, and when dealing with disease, our bodies should be washed with running water.

**\*\*\* Did You Know? \*\*\***

The Bible is the first book ever printed on a printing press, and even though many have tried to destroy the Bible, it continues to be the most widely published book. More books have been written about Jesus, the Son of God, and His teachings than anybody else in history.

swing. I'm not making it up. The Bible has a lot of scientific facts that were only discovered recently."

Sophia hopped on another swing. "Where did everything happen in the Bible?"

Josiah struggled to get his swing moving while standing on it. "I have an uncle who said he went to these places, but I don't know where they are."

Amanda pushed Josiah on the swing. "I don't know where the places are either, but there are people who dig up things in the ground and study them. What is that word called?"

"Do you mean archeology?" Sophia asked.

Gavin rolled his eyes. "Arky what?"

Sophia laughed. "**Archeology**."

"That's it," said Amanda. "Archeologists proved the Bible is historically correct. For example, when someone digs up dinosaur bones, we know dinosaurs are real."

> **Archeology**—Scientific study of material remains. Since the 1800s, over twenty-five thousand archeological sites have demonstrated the people, places, and events of the Bible are real.

Gavin shook his head side to side. "I bet church people just buried those things to make us think what the Bible says really happened."

Amanda pushed Sophia's swing higher. "That would be a lot of work for a lie. A bunch of people wrote the Bible over a long, long time."

> **\*\*\* Did You Know? \*\*\***
>
> Forty people from all walks of life wrote the Bible over fifteen hundred years. They wrote on different continents, and most of them never even met.

"**Nonreligious** sources also confirm what the Bible says," said Josiah. "There are people who did not believe in God, who saw Jesus, wrote He was wise, did amazing things, and confirmed events described in the Bible."

> **Nonreligious**—Having nothing to do with God and religion.

Gavin pumped his swing as high as he could, jumped off, and tumbled forward. He wiped his hands on his pants. "Guys, one day people will stop making Bibles and write something even more believable. You're wasting your time."

Josiah added, "God said His Words will never pass away. Even though some people try to destroy Bibles, more Bibles are published than any other book in history. It is the best-selling book ever."

Sophia's eyes widened, "That's amazing."

Amanda smiled. "God always kept His promises in the past, so I trust God will keep His promises in the future. Through reading the Bible and going to church, I learn a lot about God, He loves us, and wants us to love Him back. God promises in the Bible to love us."

# The Bible is believable because...

Science affirms
the Bible.

Archeological
discoveries
affirm the Bible.

Nonreligious sources
affirm the Bible.

God inspired 40
different people to write
portions of the Bible
over 1500 years.

Most widely published
book in history.

# **Chapter 3 Questions**

- - - - - - - - - - - - - - - - - - - - - - - - - - - - - - - - - - - - - - -

1.  The Bible is trustworthy because the following affirm the Bible: _____, _____ discoveries, and _____ sources. _____ in the Bible is also consistent with what happened in history. The Bible continues to be the most widely _____ book in history.

2.  The following are examples of scientific facts in the Bible: the earth is _____, the ocean contains _____, and when dealing with disease our bodies should be washed with

    _____ _____.

3.  One example of a prophecy in the Bible that came true: A prophet said Israel's Messiah (a king expected to save them) would be born in the town of _____. Jesus fulfilled this prophecy many years later when He was born in Bethlehem.

4.  Amanda reads the _____ and goes to _____ to learn more about God.

# Can Anyone Prove
# God Is Not Real?

Whoever does not love does not know
God, because God is love.

—1 John 4:8 (NIV)

**G**avin said, "Well, I've been standing here, and I don't feel God's love yet. Hey God, where are You?" He leaped on the monkey bars and peeked through them to see if God was on top of the slide. "Are You on the slide, God? Nope, I don't see You. Are You in the tunnel? Nope, not there either."

Amanda giggled and faced Gavin, "Just because you can't see something doesn't mean it doesn't exist. Even though we can't see the wind, we can see the effect of the wind. We can see the wind move leaves on a tree. In the same way, even though you can't see God, you can know He loves you, and He never changes. A person can become friends with God and talk to Him just like a friend. God is the One you should go to when you do something wrong. When you sincerely apologize to Him and try to change your behavior, you can feel God's amazing love because He **forgives** you." *How am I going to get through to them, God? Please help Gavin and Sophia understand.*

> **Forgive**—To release from punishment of bad choices.

Josiah and Sophia ran after Gavin as he took off up the hill. Amanda limped with her crutch after them, refusing to let her broken leg limit her.

"Silly, God isn't playing hide-and-seek with you," said Josiah. "God is like a friend Who is always with us. I can talk to Him any time about anything. There are times when God makes me feel warm and happy inside, just like warm hot chocolate. God wants to be every person's best friend and leader. I can't see Him, but I know He's here with me."

"Here I am, God. Where are you? Where were you when my parents got divorced?" Tears swelled in Gavin's eyes. "God, where were you when my dog got hit by a car? Where were you when my best friend moved far away?" A tear slipped down his cheek. He sat at the top of the hill and gazed at the surrounding mountains, his lips trembling "I guess God skipped over me when He looked for friends."

Amanda was speechless. *How could he have gone*

*through so much? Did I judge him too quickly?* She tugged her ear and moved it around.

Josiah sat next to Gavin. "It's not like that. God loves everyone and wants each person to choose to love Him back. God gives us freedom to make good choices. Bad decisions, sometimes our own and sometimes others', hurt us, not God."

Gavin wiped his eyes with his shirt sleeve. "I must have messed up bad, because I just asked God where He is, and I still don't feel His love."

Amanda pulled a tissue out of her pocket, handed it to Gavin, and shot a prayer up to God. *Please give me words to help his hurting heart, God.* "We all mess up," she said aloud, "but God loves us anyway. Every person will have hard times, even those who are close to God. I think God allows hard times to help us grow and help others later. Instead of running from God, He wants you to search for Him. He wants to help you through your hard times."

Gavin looked down. "If God wants to help me through hard times, where is He?"

Amanda placed her hand on Gavin's shoulder. "God is everywhere. When you search for God, He doesn't appear right in front of you and zap your pain away. Maybe something useful will come from our pain. God promises He won't give us more than we can handle. He gives us peace and hope through our hard times."

Warmth from Amanda's heart spread through her body as she understood Gavin more. She remembered times when she also questioned God because she couldn't see Him. She thought to herself, *My belief in God didn't just magically appear, either.*

The wind smashed a bubble on Sophia's cheek. She peeled it off, put it back in her mouth, and asked, "Why won't God let us see Him?"

Josiah brushed dirt off his pants. "No one has seen God, but people saw Jesus, the Son of God. I'd love to see God, but I know for certain I can feel His love and peace."

Amanda beamed and said, "Since millions of people feel

24

God's love and insist their lives were changed through their relationship with God's Son, Jesus, no one can prove God isn't real."

The bell rang, so all four of them walked back to the school building.

Josiah asked his friends, "Do you all want to come to my house tomorrow after school so we can hang out and talk more?"

Their eyes lit up, and they bumped fists.

# Chapter 4 Questions

- - - - - - - - - - - - - - - - - - - - - - - - - - - - - - - - - - - - - - - -

1. What things do you know exist that you cannot see?

   _____

   _____

   _____

   _____

   _____

2. We can know something exists that we can't see because we can see the _____ of it. For example, even though we can't see wind, we can see wind _____ leaves on trees.

3. Millions of people have had their lives changed through their _____ with God's Son, Jesus. Because of that, no one can prove God is not _____.

4. Why do you think God doesn't appear in human form in front us right now to prove to us He exists? _____

   _____

   _____

   _____

   _____

   _____

   _____

   _____

# How Has God Changed People?

For God is working in you, giving you the desire
and the power to do what pleases him.

—Philippians 2:13 (NLT)

"**F**riday at last." Sophia helped Amanda down the bus steps.

Josiah and Gavin hurried off the school bus and walked to Josiah's house. The sweet aroma of cookies greeted them from the entrance.

Blitz, Josiah's dog, caught his eye and nearly broke the window doing his happy-Josiah's-home dance.

As Josiah's mother opened the door, the giant fur ball stretched his paws on Josiah's shoulders.

Josiah dropped his backpack and received massive hugs and kisses from his buddy.

Blitz slowly approached Josiah's stranger friend. A few sniffs later, Blitz approved.

Gavin squatted to pat his back. "How did he get the name Blitz?"

"He's determined." Josiah's chin lifted. "After his trip home from the shelter, we took him to the back yard. Right away, he blitzed my uncle to save a juicy grilled hamburger from human destruction."

Gavin laughed and said, "I'll never eat near him."

Sophia reached down to pet Blitz. "He's trained now, aren't you, precious?"

"You might want to eat hamburgers in a different house, though." Amanda rubbed Blitz's chin in response to his welcome-home licks.

Josiah's mother greeted him with a hug and offered the warm cookies to him and his friends.

After savoring the gooey, chewy cookies and thanking Josiah's mom, they ran to the backyard to play.

Sophia darted for the spiral slide connected to the monkey bars.

Gavin leaped onto the monkey bars and swung his legs back and forth. "If knowing and obeying God means giving up all the fun in life, I don't want to know Him. I prefer to have a good time."

Smiling, Josiah also leaped on the monkey bars and said, "It's not like that, buddy. Having a relationship with God made me and millions of people more comfortable with life.

I still have fun like before. I just feel more peace now. Trouble happens when we or others disobey God."

Gavin rolled his eyes. "There's nothing like living with a leash around your neck."

Josiah grinned, lifted his chin up, and turned toward Gavin. "God isn't like that. He gives us rules to protect us. Can you imagine playing sports without rules? It would be crazy, and more people would get hurt."

Sophia grabbed a frisbee and hurled it for Blitz. "How do you know if you're disobeying God?"

Josiah swung himself to the top of the monkey bars where a ball rested. "In the Bible, God gave us Ten Commandments. These are God's laws He tells us to obey. Heads up, Sophia." He tossed the ball to her.

Sophia stretched her arm to catch the ball as she swooped down the slide. "Got it. Gavin, heads up." She sent the ball soaring. "What are the laws?"

Amanda said, "They're rules like don't lie, don't steal, and respect your parents. Obeying God's Ten Commandments is like having an umbrella to help reduce getting pounded by things that hurt you."

Obeying God's commandments helps protect
us from consequences we might receive from
disobeying God's commandments.

Sophia took a deep breath. Her feet pounded the grass as she raced to catch the ball. "Hey, I'm a good friend and try not to hurt anyone, even though I mess up sometimes."

Amanda's crutch tapped the ball toward Josiah. "Unfortunately, we are born with the desire to do things our way, and this desire causes us to break God's commandments. Breaking one of God's commandments is called **sin**."

Josiah leaped off the monkey bars. "No matter what we do, we are unable to obey all of God's commandments all of the time. For example, one of God's commandments is don't lie. Have you ever lied or stolen something?"

> **Sin**—A bad choice that someone makes; it separates us from God.

"Sure. I've lied about finishing my chores and stole candy from the store when my mom wouldn't let me have it." Sophia sat on the tire swing. "I didn't kill anyone, though."

Gavin bumped the ball toward Amanda. "I do more good things than bad things. No one is perfect."

Amanda whacked the ball with her crutch, lost her balance, and landed on her stomach with a moan. She pondered, *God, when is my leg going to heal?*

"Are you okay?" asked Josiah.

Sophia rushed to help her.

Blitz ran to Amanda with the frisbee.

"Yes, I'm okay. Thanks, Blitz." Amanda rolled on her back, sighed, and tossed the frisbee. "How do you know for certain the good things you do in your life outweigh your bad choices?"

"I don't think anyone can measure that," Sophia said, picking up Amanda's crutch and handing it to her.

Josiah's foot thrust the ball upward. His knee bumped it up again and again. "You're right. It's impossible to measure whether your good outweighs your bad. God views all sin equally bad because any sin is hurtful. It doesn't matter if you stole a piece of bubblegum or murdered someone, both are equally sinful. God's love is perfect, and He holds us accountable for obeying His commandments."

Amanda wobbled over to the tire swing. "God knows we

can't obey His commandments all the time. What's super cool is God provides a way for us to repair the separation sin creates in our relationship with Him, so we can be His friend. After you establish a relationship with God, your guilt from your previous bad choices gets washed away."

Sophia twisted the tire swing as much as she could and hopped on with Amanda. The swing spun around and around.

The spinning slowed; Amanda leaned back and looked up at Gavin. "People all over the world are more content with their life after they became friends with Jesus." Her eyes sparkled. "Obeying God and being friends with Him gave me more peace about things, even in hard times. It's different from excitement you feel when you get a gift or eat your favorite food."

Amanda crawled out of the tire swing and reached for her crutches.

Sophia said, "So after you accepted God's gift of love and forgiveness, do you no longer have hard times?"

Amanda laughed as she looked at her broken leg. "I wish there were no more hard times. Life still has troubles, pain, and sadness, but God promises to help us through our hard times. It's our own bad choices, and sometimes those of other people, that cause us pain, not God." She grabbed the swing chain and shook it. "Just like we trust this swing to hold us, it feels good to trust God will help us."

Gavin threw his hands up in the air. "It's frustrating not to be able to see God."

Blitz ran to Gavin, dropped the frisbee, and nudged him until he began petting him.

"I wish I could see God too." Amanda sat with Gavin, and Blitz rolled on his back. "You know, even though I can't see the wind, I enjoy seeing the effects of the wind." She pointed at a blue bird singing and surfing the breeze. "As one breeze carries the bird higher, the bird takes an adventurous dip and is lifted by the next cool breeze. It's the same with God's love. Even though you can't see God's love, you can feel the result of it in your heart, mind, and soul. You can also see the result of God's love in people who have a relationship with Him; it changes their behavior in a good way."

"Just like the wind moves leaves on trees, God moves people to share His love with others," added Josiah. "When you accept the gift of God's love and forgiveness, He gives you special gifts, **spiritual gifts** that you can use to serve Him and help others." He slid down the slide and hopped on the swing. "It pleases God when we help people. God will lead you to do things for others that are more meaningful than pursuing good things for only yourself."

Gavin replied, "So it's okay with God to be His friend and still have fun?"

Josiah flew forward off the swing. His feet crunched the leaves.

> **Spiritual gift**—A special talent that God gives you. Examples of spiritual gifts include leadership, teaching, encouragement, mercy, evangelism, discernment, wisdom, giving, and help.

"Absolutely. God wants you to enjoy life. Every person will still have hard times, though."

Gavin tossed the frisbee for Blitz. "So what's next?"

"The clubhouse?" Josiah suggested.

"I meant about knowing God," said Gavin.

"Oh." Josiah said, "God wants us to talk to Him anytime, anywhere, and about anything. He also wants us to learn more about Him, so we can love others more."

# **Chapter 5 Questions**

- - - - - - - - - - - - - - - - - - - - - - - - - - - - - - - - - - - - - - - - - - -

1. People are more _____ with their lives when having a relationship with God.

2. People still have _____ _____ after becoming friends with God. But God promises to _____ us through our hard times.

3. Other peoples' bad choices and sometimes our own bad choices cause us _____, not God.

4. Even though we can't see God, millions of people can feel the effect of God's _____ in their hearts, minds, and actions.

5. If you already have a relationship with God, how is your life different from before? _____

_____

_____

_____

_____

_____

_____

_____

_____

_____

_____

_____

_____

_____

_____

_____

_____

6. A spiritual gift is a special _____ God gives you after you become friends with Him and begin a relationship with Him. God wants us to use our special talents to help others and serve Him.

7. What spiritual gifts do you think God gave you? Examples of spiritual gifts include serving, teaching, encouragement, giving, administration, and compassion. An excellent resource for discovering and growing children's gifts is *Discover Your Children's Gifts* by Don and Katie Fortune. _____

_____

_____

_____

_____

_____

# 6

# Who Is the Real God?

Whoever does not love does not know
God, because God is love.

—1 John 4:8 (NIV)

J osiah and Sophia raced up the climbing wall to the clubhouse, while Gavin tried to beat them to it by running up the slide. Amanda and Blitz worked their way up the clubhouse ramp.

Gavin crawled through the slide entrance. His eyes widened when he saw race car tracks, cars, and sports trophies along the clubhouse walls. "Wow, how did you win all these awards?"

Josiah plopped down in a bean bag chair near Sophia and Amanda. "I played a lot of soccer and volleyball games."

Blitz worked his way into Josiah's lap and licked his face.

Josiah laughed and said, "You're not a puppy anymore, Blitz."

Soon they were taking in the smoky aroma of a neighbor grilling steaks. The breeze rocked the branches, and the leaves rustled. A squirrel bounced across a tree branch. In that brief moment, one could feel the thickness of Josiah and Amanda's excitement, coupled with Gavin's distrust about God.

Sophia reached for a marker and began drawing a flower on the whiteboard. "I want to learn more about God. What should I do?"

Josiah grinned and answered, "God tells us who He is in the Bible, so you can start learning about God by reading the Bible and going to church." He grabbed a Bible from a clubhouse bookshelf and handed it to Sophia. "You can borrow this one if you want."

Sophia smiled, looked steadily into his eyes, and said, "Thanks."

Gavin crossed his arms. "What does God look like?"

Amanda closed her eyes. *God, please give me the words to help Gavin and Sophia understand you.* She scooted near the whiteboard and said, "Sophia, may I borrow the marker?"

"Sure." Sophia tossed the marker to her.

With her shoulders back and chin up, Amanda drew a picture on the whiteboard. "The Bible tells us there is one God made of three distinct individuals: the **Father**, the **Son** (**Jesus**), and the **Holy Spirit**."

Sophia scratched her head. "I can imagine the Father

having a spirit. However, if there is just one God, why is there both a Father and a Son? I'm confused. It seems like there is more than one God."

Amanda drew a picture of an egg. "You know how an egg has three parts: the egg shell, yolk, and white? Even though it has three parts, it is still just one egg. Each part has a different function. The shell protects, the yolk supplies food, and the white helps keep the yolk in the center."

Gavin studied the car he held. "The egg functions are neat, but what does that have to do with God?"

Amanda drew another picture next to the egg and continued, "Just like parts of an egg have different functions, the Father, Son, and Holy Spirit also have different functions. The Father created a plan for us to have a relationship with God, the Son (Jesus) fulfilled that plan, and the Holy Spirit helps guide us with wisdom and understanding."

Josiah added, "God is all-loving and never changes. He never hurts us because he is perfect. God allows us to go through hard times but He promises to help us through our hard times. He always existed and always will. God is much more complex than we are. It's okay to have questions about God. Our questions will be answered when we read the Bible, and go to church."

Amanda shot up a quick prayer in her mind: *Thanks for the help, God.*

# Chapter 6 Questions

- - - - - - - - - - - - - - - - - - - - - - - - - - - - - - - - - - - - - -

1. What does God look like? God is made of _____ distinct individuals: the _____, the _____, and the _____ _____.

2. What does each individual of God do? The Father _____ a plan for us to have a relationship with God. Jesus _____ the plan. The Holy Spirit _____ us.

3. God never causes suffering because He is _____. He is pure and completely separate from anything that is _____. God does allow us to go through hard times and helps us through our hard times.

4. God is all-_____ and never _____.

# Why Should I Be Friends with God?

God so loved the world that he gave his one and only Son. Anyone who believes in him will not die but will have eternal life.
—John 3:16 (NIrV)

For He Himself is our peace.
—Ephesians 2:14a (NIV)

Sophia asked, "I love my parents, teacher, friends, and I know they love me too. Why should I care about my relationship with God? I can't even see Him."

Josiah turned toward Sophia and said, "You can't see love or hurt, either. But if you had the choice to feel love or pain, which would you choose?"

"Of course I would choose love. I want to feel good." Sophia shrugged her shoulders.

"Me too," said Gavin.

Josiah smiled at their answers. "The reason God created us is because He loves us, and wants us to freely choose to love Him back."

Amanda beamed, "When you become friends with God, you get to experience all His love, which is better than love from anyone else. God's love is so big I can't wrap my arms around it. When I do something wrong, I feel guilty and seek forgiveness. Then God's love empties my heart of **guilt** I feel because of the bad things I've done. God loves you no matter what you do,

> **Guilt**—A bad or heavy feeling of responsibility for having done something wrong.

> **Heaven**—Place where the spirits of those who chose to be friends with God (establish a saving relationship through Jesus) reside after their physical body dies.

> **Hell**—An evil place of torture and eternal separation from God. This is where the spirits of those who chose not to be friends with God reside after their physical body dies.

and He cares about every detail of your life. He even knows the number of hairs on our head."

Josiah looked at Gavin and Sophia. "The most important decision you will make in your life is your decision to have a relationship with God. Your decision determines whether you'll spend eternity in a loving place (**Heaven**) with God or separated from Him forever in an evil, painful place (**hell**)."

Choose to have a relationship with God.

Choose to remain separated from God.

Your Most Important Decision Ever

Amanda looked at Gavin and Sophia and explained, "God promises one day He will separate those who choose to love Him from those who don't. However, God first gives every person the opportunity to love Him back and clean their heart."

A breeze passed through the window and rearranged Amanda's hair. She pulled her hair away from her face, "God is patient and gives us multiple chances. But the time to choose will eventually run out because God promises one day, He will separate those who love Him from those who don't. That day could be today, tomorrow, or next year. No one knows when that time will be, except God."

"I'll think about it." Gavin jumped up off the floor and gazed out the window.

Amanda reached for her crutch and pondered, *What is there to think about? God, please help him.*

"What are the piles of sand and stone for?" Gavin asked, sliding down the escape pole and running over to the piles.

"My dad is building a patio and fire pit over there. Wait." Josiah grabbed the zip line and soared out of the clubhouse.

"No way. Those are for building a fort to protect us from intruders," Sophia said, jumping up and following Gavin. "Last one there is a rotten egg."

Amanda swooped down the clubhouse slide and hobbled over to the piles of sand and stone.

Blitz trotted down the ramp and explored the yard.

Sophia began building a fort wall with the stones.

Gavin sifted smooth white sand through his fingers. "I'm getting more curious about God, but I still have trouble loving what I can't see."

"I understand." Amanda's finger carved a path for an ant. "I used to think the same way. God promises if we search for Him, we'll find Him. So never give up searching. You may not see God, but He exists, wants you to love Him back, and will help you."

Josiah added, "There's a thick wall between God and us called sin because we all disobey God. Sin creates distance between God and us because God is sinless and cannot stand sin. We need to get through this wall to be friends with God."

Gavin shrugged and said, "That's okay. I still love my friends even if they live far away. I can love God from a distance too."

Amanda's face dropped. "The separation sin creates between God and us is different from the distance that separates us from some of our friends. You can decide to visit your friend and remove the distance between you. But after you die, you can't change your mind about being friends with God. After our body dies, our spirit lives forever in either a loving place, in close relationship with God, or in a painful place separated from Him."

Gavin rolled his eyes so hard they almost popped out of his head, "Lighten up, Amanda. So what if there's some separation between God and us? He knows we aren't perfect."

Sophia smirked and said, "I have a friend who moved away. Distance separates us, but we're still friends. If God knows everything, then He knows I care, even though I make mistakes."

Amanda scooted closer to Gavin and Sophia. "God isn't just another friend."

Sophia snapped her fingers together. "I got it. I'll just plan not to sin, tell God I love Him, and look for ways to help others."

Amanda shot up a quick prayer: *God, I need some help here.* She shook her head slowly. "Sophia, that won't establish a relationship with God. The bad choices you already made still separate you from God. God is holy, pure, and completely separate from anything that is impure."

# **Chapter 7 Questions**

- - - - - - - - - - - - - - - - - - - - - - - - - - - - - - - - - - - -

1.  Amanda realized she sinned and her _____ separates her from God. Have you ever disobeyed your parents or done something wrong when you thought no one saw you?

2.  Sin separates us from God because God is _____ (pure) and is completely separate from anything that is _____.

3.  After we die physically, our spirit will either live forever with God surrounded by love or separated from God in _____. Eternal separation from God is spiritual death.

4.  There is nothing we can do to make up for our _____ and work our way to God.

5.  Why do you think someone would not want to be friends with God? _____

    _____

    _____

    _____

    _____

    _____

    _____

    _____

    _____

6.  If you are not friends with God, do you want to be friends with God now? _____

# How Can I Be Friends with God?

Say with your mouth, "Jesus is Lord." Believe in your heart that God raised him from the dead. Then you will be **saved**.

—Romans 10:9 (NIrV)

**Saved**—Forgiven forever for your sins by God and in a loving relationship with Him. One day, God will separate all those in a relationship with Him from all evil.

"**S**o if we've all messed up and made bad choices, how do we fix the sin and be friends with God?" Sophia crossed her arms over her chest.

"Unfortunately, there's nothing we can do to fix the sin." Amanda looked down.

Gavin expressed his solution with his usual enthusiasm: "I got it. I'll create a time machine so we can go back in time and choose to make good choices instead of bad ones. That way, our sin won't come between God and us."

Sophia laughed and clapped her hands. "Great idea, Gavin."

"I wish we could do that," Josiah said with a half-smile. "If only we could create that time machine. I would love to take back mean things I've said or done and the hurt I caused."

Amanda said, "God could have created a time machine so we could go back in time, but He didn't. Somehow, God has a way of using even our bad choices for good."

"What do you mean?" asked Sophia. "How can bad choices be turned to good?"

Amanda gathered her thoughts for a minute and then said, "Here's an example: I've seen a bully pick on a younger, soft-spoken kid. Instead of being angry or hurt, the younger kid said to the bully, 'I hope you feel better about yourself someday.' Later, the bully apologized and asked the younger kid why he was so nice. The good part is the younger kid spoke to the bully about God, which helped the bully establish a relationship with God. Now, the two of them are friends."

Gavin placed his hands on his hips and tilted his head. "Okay, tell me how God will use my parents' divorce for good?"

"That's a hard one." Amanda looked down at the sand. "I'm sorry you and your family went through that. It's hard for imperfect people to live together, but God teaches ways to make it easier in the Bible."

Josiah picked up a ball and tossed it to Gavin; he said, "We might not understand how God uses bad choices for good or how God does a lot of things, but that's okay. God knows everything and is in control. At some point, you just need to trust God like you trust the monkey bars to hold you when you hang on them."

Sophia stepped onto a short stone wall, her arms thrown to the side of her body for balance. "How do we become friends with God?"

Amanda smoothed out an area of sand. "Hold on a minute." She grabbed two large rocks, a few stones, and a couple of sticks and then sat down next to the sand pile. "Pretend these two big rocks are mountains." She placed two large rocks two feet apart from each other in the sand. "Think about man being on one mountain and God being on the other. There's a big **barrier** in between them called sin." She used her stick to write the word "sin" in big letters in between the two rocks. "Sin separates us from God."

> **Barrier**—Something that blocks moving from one place to another.

Sin Separates Us from God

Amanda placed two small stones next to the rock labelled "man." "Some people try to work their way to God by doing good deeds like feeding the poor or helping someone." She placed another small stone. "Other people try to get closer to God by going to church." She placed the final small stone next to the others. "Some people give money. They try to build a bridge over their sin to get to God, but it's not enough. Sin still separates us from God, and there's nothing we can do to make up for it."

Some People Try to Work Their Way to God,
but Sin Still Separates Them from God

Gavin kicked the sand. "That's just great. Our sin drove God so far away, we'll never find Him."

Sophia looked down and rubbed the back of her neck; she said, "I guess I'll never know God, either, because I've made a bunch of bad choices too."

Amanda lifted her palms and said, "Wait. It's not like that. Every person sins because we are unable to obey God all of the time. The great news is God made a way to rescue us from our sin."

Amanda placed one stick vertically in the sand over the word "sin" and laid the other stick horizontally over it. "God sent His Son, Jesus, to take our punishment for our sins by dying on the cross for us. Three days later, God raised Him from the dead. When He did this, Jesus **Christ** lovingly made a way (a bridge) for us to be friends with God so we won't have to be separated from Him forever."

> **Christ**—The title for Jesus which means Jesus was sent by God to be a King and a Deliverer from the penalty of sin.

God Made One Way for Us to Establish a Relationship
with Him when He Sent His Son, Jesus Christ

61

"Why would God do that to His Son?" Gavin shook his head side to side.

Sophia looked down and said, "That doesn't sound very loving."

Amanda prayed silently, *God, how can we help Gavin and Sophia understand You?*

Josiah said, "God knew the only response to sin that can truly change people is a loving and just response." Jesus never sinned and is all-loving. He willingly suffered the punishment for our sin to rescue us from being separated from God forever.

Sophia looked away. "How is that just?"

Silence gushed over Josiah as his chin lowered to his chest. Then Josiah's eyes lit up, "If a child is bullied at school and a teacher doesn't deal with it, the teacher would not be just. God is just because He dealt with sin. Jesus could have removed Himself from the cross, but He chose to pay the penalty for our sin. What Jesus did is give us a free gift, the best gift ever. All we need to do is choose to receive this gift."

Gavin stood taller, puffed his chest out, and asked, "How do I ask God for this gift? Do I have to be at church?"

Josiah said, "No, you can ask God anywhere. You can talk to Him on the playground, at school, in your bed, or anywhere. God can hear you, even if you just think the words you want to say to Him in your mind. To receive this free gift and establish a relationship with God, say a prayer like this: Dear God, I'm sorry for my bad choices. Please forgive my sin. I believe Jesus died for my sin and rose again. Please be my Savior, Lord, and Friend."

Amanda's eyes teared up. "After you accept God's gift, what Jesus did on the cross for you, and sincerely ask God to forgive your sins,

| |
|---|
| **Friend**—One you trust, spend time with, and talk to. |

| |
|---|
| **Savior**—Deliverer from the punishment of sin. |

| |
|---|
| **Lord**—One who has power and authority over another. |

| |
|---|
| **Holy Spirit**—One of the three persons of God. The Holy Spirit guides those who establish a relationship with God. |

God places the Holy Spirit in you to help guide you to make good choices. At this point you can be sure God forgave your sins and made your heart clean."

Sophia couldn't hold back the excitement; she said, "After I establish a relationship with God, may I sin as much as I want?"

Amanda's head dropped in her hands.

Gavin smiled. "Oh yeah, and does it mean I can also skip my chores and homework?"

Josiah laughed. "No way. You might still sin, but you'll feel the Holy Spirit warning you not to. You will still receive consequences for your sin. As you grow closer to God, you will want to obey Him and will feel better when you do."

# Chapter 8 Questions

- - - - - - - - - - - - - - - - - - - - - - - - - - - - - - - - - - - - - -

1. Is there a sin barrier between you and God? Yes/No. There is a sin barrier if you ever broke any of God's commandments:

   - Put God first.
   - Worship God only.
   - Use God's name with respect.
   - Rest one day a week.
   - Respect your parents.
   - Don't hurt others.
   - Be faithful to your husband or wife.
   - Don't steal.
   - Be honest.
   - Don't envy.

Hint: Every human being has broken at least one of God's commandments, so we all need to receive God's gift, Jesus, to have a relationship with Him.

2. The penalty for sin is _____ _____ which is eternal separation from God.

3. God sent his Son, _____ _____ to help communicate His _____ to us, pay the penalty for our sin, and make the way for us to have a relationship with Him.

4. We can have a _____ ("be friends") with God after we overcome the sin barrier between us and _____ by believing what Jesus did for us and asking for forgiveness. This requires a genuine acceptance of what God did for us and a desire to obey God (change our heart).

5.  To overcome the sin barrier between yourself and God, you can _____ the following prayer (or something similar): "Dear God, I'm sorry for my sin. Please forgive me. I believe Jesus paid the penalty for my sin. Please be my Savior, Lord, and Friend."

6.  After you accept God's gift (Jesus) and ask for forgiveness for your sins, God places the _____ _____ in you to help guide you to make good choices.

7.  Is it okay to sin after you become friends with God? Yes/ No. Why? _____

    _____

    _____

    _____

    _____

    _____

8.  After you have a relationship with God, if you realize you sin, ask God to _____ you and _____ your behavior to obey God.

9.  Do you want to establish a relationship ("be friends") with God? Yes/No. If yes, you can pray the following prayer (or something similar): "Dear God, I'm sorry for my sin. Please forgive me. I believe Jesus paid the penalty for my sin and rose again. Please be my Savior, Lord, and Friend."

10. How is being "friends" with God different from being friends with people you know? _____

    _____

    _____

    _____

    _____

    _____

_____

_____

11. God created us so we can freely choose to establish a _____ with Him. The Bible tells us God gives everyone evidence of His existence. So there is no excuse not to establish a relationship with Him.

# What Should I Do after I Become Friends with God?

Don't worry about anything; instead, pray about everything. Tell God what you need, and thank him for all he has done. Then you will experience God's peace, which exceeds anything we can understand. His peace will guard your hearts and minds as you live in Christ Jesus.

—Philippians 4:6–7 (NLT)

The tree shadows grew longer. The sun kissed their cheeks. Josiah's mother shouted out the back door, "Ten more minutes until dinner."

"Okay, Mom," Josiah leaned forward and tossed an adoring glance at his mom.

Blitz dashed after leaves falling from a tree.

"What's popping, Sophia?" asked Amanda. *I wonder what she's thinking?*

Sophia shrugged her shoulders. An enormous bubble popped and then smacked her cheek. Peeling the gum off of her face, she asked, "After you start a relationship with God, what do you do next?"

Gavin tossed a handful of sand at Sophia's legs and said, "Where do you come up with these questions?"

Amanda laughed and said, "The questions are great. There are several ways to learn more about God and become better friends with Him. You can ask your parents to take you to a church that teaches the Bible, ask God to help you make better choices, and talk to God (pray). Talking to God is like talking to a friend. When you pray, you can thank God for all He does, tell Him your sins, and ask Him to help you and others through struggles."

> **Baptized**—An outward expression that you trust Jesus as Lord and Savior. Baptism is not a requirement to establish a relationship with God but it is an act of obedience. Baptisms in the Bible were carried out by submerging a person briefly under water which symbolizes the death of the person's sinful old life just as Jesus died for the punishment for our sins. Just as Jesus rose from the dead and lives forever, a person getting baptized rises out of the water to represent walking in the new life with Jesus as your Lord and Savior.

Josiah stood up and brushed sand off his pants. "I understand God better when I read the Bible and talk about questions. The Bible tells us to get **baptized** after we establish a relationship with God."

Josiah smiled and looked at Gavin and Sophia; he suggested, "Why don't you and your families come to the

Fall Festival at our church this weekend? You can meet more people, and I'll show you around. If you like it, you can come to church with us on Sunday."

"I'm in," said Sophia as another bubble exploded on her face.

Gavin stood up and wiped his forehead with his sleeve. "I'm not sure I believe everything you said about God, but I'll come hang out."

Sophia extended her hand to help Amanda, who wobbled to her feet.

"I'm glad you both will come with us," Amanda said. "As you learn more about God and let Him use you to love and help others, He will make more sense to you. Your life will still have hard times, but trust God and He will help you."

Peace surrounded Amanda as she realized it was not her job to convince others that God is real. She breathed in cool air and exhaled the burden she carried. *Even though I don't have all the answers, God can still use me to love and help people. When people search for God, He will soften their hearts so they can learn to love Him and others more. God just wants me to be prepared to answer why I believe in Him and have hope for my eternal future in heaven.*

Fall Festival

# **Chapter 9 Questions**

- - - - - - - - - - - - - - - - - - - - - - - - - - - - - - - - - - - - - - - -

1.  After you establish a relationship with God, how can you grow closer to Him?

   _____
   _____
   _____
   _____
   _____
   _____
   _____

2.  Why is it important to know why you believe in God? __

   _____
   _____
   _____
   _____
   _____
   _____
   _____

3.  Name ways God can use you to love and help others more?

   _____
   _____
   _____
   _____
   _____
   _____
   _____

# Glossary

**Accurate** Correct.

**Administration** A gift that God gives some people. It is reflected in many ways including being organized, excellent communicator, enthusiastic, goal-driven, strong leader, and loves being around people.

**Archeology** "The scientific study of material remains (as fossil relics, artifacts, and monuments) of past human life and activities." Since the 1800s, thousands of archeological sites have demonstrated that the people, places, and events of the Bible are real.

**Baptism** An outward expression that a person trusts Jesus as Lord and Savior and established a relationship with God. Just like a wedding ring is not a requirement to be married, baptism is not a requirement to establish a relationship with God. After a person establishes a relationship with God, the next step is to get baptized. Baptism is a symbol of Jesus Christ's burial and resurrection. When we go under the water, we bury the old life and when we rise above the water, we walk in a new life with Jesus as Lord and Savior.

**Barrier** Something that blocks moving from one place to another.

**Bible** The collection of holy writings, inspired by God. The Bible is the Christian scriptures and contains sixty-six books. There are two major parts of the Bible: Old Testament and New Testament.

"This God-inspired book called the Bible was written during a 1500-year span through more than 40 generations by more than 40 different authors from every walk of life—shepherds, soldiers, prophets, poets, monarchs, scholars, statesmen, masters, servants, tax collectors, fishermen, and tentmakers. Its God-breathed words were written in a variety of places: the wilderness, in a palace, in a dungeon, on a hillside, in a prison, and in exile. It was penned on the continents of Asia, Africa, and Europe and was written in three languages: Hebrew, Aramaic, and Greek. It tells hundreds of stories, records hundreds of songs, and addresses hundreds of controversial subjects. Yet with all its variety of authors, origins, and content, it achieves a miraculous continuity of theme—God's **redemption** of his children and the restoration of all things to His original design." (***The Unshakable Truth,*** **www.harvesthousepublishers.com**)

**Christ** The title for Jesus which means Jesus was sent by God to be a King and a Deliverer from the penalty of sin.

**Christian** Follower of Jesus Christ.

**Church** A gathering of people united to learn about and worship God, who respond to God by faith in God's grace through Jesus. They are God's hands and feet in loving other people.

**Commandments** God's laws that He wants all people to obey.

**Confusion** Disorder, chaos, lack of clearness.

**Cross** Two wooden beams connected to form a standing frame which could support a body. Jesus took the punishment for our sins by choosing to suffer and die on a cross so we can establish our relationship with God.

**Crucifixion** The act of killing someone by nailing or tying their hands and feet to a cross. Jesus allowing Himself to be crucified as a sacrifice for our sins.

**Death** There are two kinds of death: physical and spiritual. In physical death, a person's physical body dies, but the person's spirit lives forever. Spiritual death is separation from God.

**Deceive** To mislead.

**Defense** Argument for believing in something.

**Eternal** Lasts forever.

**Eternity** Forever, having no end.

**Evangelism** Presenting Jesus Christ to others in the power of the Holy Spirit. The goal is to help others establish a relationship with God by accepting Jesus as their Lord and Savior and live their lives for God.

**Evil** Morally wrong as defined by the Bible. Hurtful due to bad behavior.

**Faith** Belief and confidence in God.

**Father** God, the Father: one of the three persons of God (the other two persons are Jesus and the Holy Spirit). God the Father defined the plan for us to repair our relationship with Him.

**Forgive** To stop feeling angry or resentful toward others and release them from penalty of bad choices.

**Forgiveness** The release from penalty of bad choices.

**Friend** One you trust, spend time with, and talk with.

**Fruits of the Spirit** The result of the Holy Spirit working in a person who chose to be friends with God. The Bible tells us in Galatians 5:22 (NIV), "But the fruit of the Spirit is love, joy, peace, forbearance, kindness, goodness, faithfulness, gentleness, and self-control."

**Fulfill** Put into effect. Meet the requirement. Implement.

**Fulfilled** Met the requirement.

**Fulfilling** Providing satisfaction. Feeling that one's talent is fully used.

**God** All-loving creator of the universe. There are three persons of God: Father, Son, and Holy Spirit. All three are one God. It's okay to have questions about God and not fully understand Him. God even tells us He is incomprehensible in the Bible ("How great is God—beyond our understanding!" Job 36:26a NIV) Some attributes of God include perfect, eternal, holy, gracious, faithful, kind, righteous, unique, truth, accessible, love, just, patient, good, forgiving, merciful, never changes, majestic.

**Grace** God giving us what we don't deserve (God's love at the expense of His son, Jesus). Undeserved kindness, mercy, assistance.

**Guilt** A bad or heavy feeling of responsibility for having done something wrong.

**Heaven** Place where the spirit of those who chose to establish a saving relationship with God reside after their physical body dies. In Revelation 21:4 (NIV), the Bible says, "[God] will wipe every tear from their eyes. There will be no more death, mourning or crying or pain, for the old order of things has passed away."

**Hell** An evil place of torture and eternal separation from God. It was created for Satan and his helpers (demons). This is where the spirit of those who chose not to be friends with God reside after their physical body dies.

**Historical** Having once existed.

**Holy** Perfect, sinless.

**Holy Spirit** The Holy Spirit is one of the three persons of God (the other two persons are the Father and Jesus). The Holy Spirit guides and teaches us.

**Hope** The feeling that what you want can be had.

**Internet** A vast computer network linking smaller computer networks worldwide.

**Jesus** Son of God: one of the three persons of God (the other two persons are the Father and the Holy Spirit). Jesus is the one and only true way to God. He fulfilled the plan for removing the wall of sin between us and God.

**Just** Behaving according to what is morally right. The Bible says "For all have sinned and fall short of the glory of God." (Romans 3:23 NKJV) In other words, every person has sinned. The Bible also says the penalty for sin is death: "For the wages of sin is death, but the gift of God is eternal life in Christ Jesus our Lord." (Romans 6:23 NKJV) God is just because He deals with sin through Jesus Christ. If someone is bullied at school and the teacher does nothing, the teacher is not just.

**KJV** King James Version (of the Bible).

**Life Group** A small group of people that get together on a regular basis (usually once a week or month) to learn more about God, encourage and help each other, work together as a group to help others, play games, eat together, go on fun outings together. The people come from varied backgrounds, and many in a church belong to several of these groups.

**Lord** One who has power and authority over others and whom service and obedience is due.

**Love** Strong affection toward someone else. Bible definition: "Love is patient. Love is kind. It does not want what belongs to others. It does not brag. It is not proud. It does not dishonor other people. It does not look out for its own interests. It does not easily become angry. It does not keep track of other people's wrongs. Love is not happy with evil. But it is full of joy when the truth is spoken. It always protects. It always trusts. It always hopes. It never gives up." (1 Corinthians 13:4–7 NIRV).

**Mercy** Not getting punished, even if you deserve it.

**Messiah** Jesus Christ. The Jews refer to the Messiah as a king who is expected to save them.

**Moral** Conforms to commands of right conduct. God tells us about His commands of right conduct in the Holy Bible.

**NIrV** New International Reader's Version (of the Bible).

**NIV** New International Version (of the Bible).

**NKJV** New King James Version (of the Bible). Easier for children to read than the KJV.

**NLT** New Living Translation (of the Bible).

**Nonreligious** Having nothing to do with God and religion.

**Perfect** Without flaw or defect.

**Physical** Relating to the body that you can touch.

**Pray** Talk to God. Prayers could include thanking God, asking God, confessing to God, and praising God.

**Prophecy** A declaration that something will happen in the future.

**Prophet** A person who God inspires to warn of the future and provide guidance. There are prophets from God, and there are also false prophets. Deuteronomy 18:21–22 documents the test for identifying a prophet of God. The last seventeen books of the Old Testament are about the prophets. God's prophets are accurate 100 percent of the time in all of their predictions of the future. False prophets (people speaking for Satan) are not always accurate in their predictions.

**Pure** Free from defect or blemish.

**Reason** The explanation for a belief. "But make sure that in your hearts you honor Christ as Lord. Always be ready to give an answer to anyone who asks you about the hope you have. Be ready to give the reason for it. But do it gently and with respect" (1 Peter 3:15 NIrV).

**Redeem** To make amends for; to clear by payment.

**Redemption** The act of saving people from sin or evil.

**Reject** Refuse to accept.

**Relationship** The way two or more beings deal with each other.

**Reliable** Trustworthy.

**Repent** To feel bad for something wrong you did and want to change to do what is right.

**Repentance** The act of repenting.

**Righteous** Acting in a moral way.

**Salvation** "Deliverance from the power and effects of sin."

**Saved** Forgiven for your sins and in a loving relationship with God forever. One day, God will separate all those in a relationship with Him from evil. After our physical body dies, our spirit will either live forever in heaven with God or be separated from Him (live forever in hell).

**Savior** Jesus, the Son of God, who delivers those who believe in Him from the punishment of sin (spiritual death).

**Scripture** The Holy Bible.

**Serve God** Help others, help the church, and help more people establish and grow their relationship with God.

**Serving** A gift that God gives some people. It is reflected in many ways: working with your hands, completing a job, liking to help, and showing love for others in your actions.

**Sin** Bad choices people make. Bad decisions are those that cause you to disobey God in your mind, actions, or words. Sin is something wrong you do but can also be something right you avoided doing. Sin separates us from God.

**Son** Jesus, God the Son. One of the three persons of God. The other two persons of God are the Father and the Holy Spirit. The Son fulfilled God the Father's plan for us to establish a relationship with God.

**Soul** The spiritual part of a human, which is separate from the physical part and survives the physical death.

**Spirit** The soul which separates from the physical body at death.

**Spiritual Gift** God gives every person who becomes friends with Him special talent(s) to use to help others and serve God. Examples of spiritual gifts include leadership, teaching, encouragement, mercy, evangelism, discernment, wisdom, giving, and helping others.

**Spiritual Gift Test** A tool for determining how the Holy Spirit equipped you to serve God. Many spiritual gift tests are available on the Internet.

**Spiritually** Relating to religious things.

**Ten Commandments** Ten laws that God wants every person to obey.

**Tribulation** Pain or suffering.

**Trustworthy** Believable.

**Unrighteousness** Unfair or unjust; sinful.

**Wisdom** Knowledge of right and wrong together with good (according to the Bible) judgment on the actions to take.

# Discussion Question Answers

The following answers aid parents, leaders, and teachers with the discussion questions. If you have comments or recommendations for additional questions, please send them to IsGodRealKids@gmail.com.

**Chapter 1: Why Do You Think God Is Real?**

2. Amanda believes God is real because only God can create <u>something</u> from <u>nothing</u>.

   "In the beginning God created the heavens and the earth." (Genesis 1:1 NKJV)

**Chapter 2: How Can You Create Something from Nothing?**

1. God tells us how the world was created in the <u>Bible</u>.

   "In the beginning God created heaven and earth." (Genesis 1:1: NIrV)

   "The heavens declare the glory of God; the skies proclaim the work of his hands." (Psalm 19:1 NIV)

2. Several organizations specialize in educating people on creation, including Creation Today (<u>www.creationtoday.org</u>), Creation Network (<u>www.creationnetwork.org</u>), and Institute for Creation Research (<u>www.icr.org</u>).

## Chapter 3: Why Trust the Bible?

1. The Bible is trustworthy because the following affirm the Bible: <u>science</u>, <u>archeological</u> discoveries, and <u>nonreligious</u> sources. <u>Prophecy</u> in the Bible is also consistent with what happened in history. The Bible continues to be the most widely <u>published</u> book in history.

   • Prophecy in the Bible is consistent with what happened in history. Therefore, it's easier to believe what the Bible says about other future events. "Above all, here is what you must understand. No prophecy in Scripture ever came from a prophet's own understanding of things. Prophecy never came simply because a prophet wanted it to. Instead, the Holy Spirit guided the prophets as they spoke. So, although prophets are human, prophecy comes from God" (2 Peter 1:20–21 NIrV).
   • Many scientific facts were documented in the Bible long before they were discovered, proven, and accepted.
   • Throughout history, nonreligious resources confirm the accuracy of events specified in the Bible.
   • Thousands of archeological findings prove the Bible is historically accurate.
   • God always kept His promises in the past, so we can be certain He will keep His promises for the future.

Even though every event documented in the Bible can't be repeated in a classroom science lab, God did inspire over forty authors in the Bible to reveal His character and desire to have a loving relationship with us. Amanda and Josiah give several reasons we can believe what the Bible says is from God.

"All Scripture is given by inspiration of God, and is profitable for doctrine, for reproof, for correction, for instruction in righteousness, that the man of God may be complete, thoroughly equipped for every good work." (2 Timothy 3:16 NKJV)

2. The following are examples of scientific facts in the Bible that were not known when the Bible was written: The earth is <u>round</u>, the ocean contains <u>springs</u>, and when dealing with disease our bodies should be washed with <u>running</u> <u>water</u>.

   "God sits above the circle of the earth. The people below seem like grasshoppers to him! He spreads out the heavens like a curtain and makes his tent from them." (Isaiah 40:22 NLT)

   "Have you traveled to the springs at the bottom of the ocean? Have you walked in its deepest parts?" (Job 38:16 NIrV)

   "And when he who has a discharge is cleansed of his discharge, then he shall count for himself seven days for his cleansing, wash his clothes, and bathe his body in running water; then he shall be clean." (Lev 15:13 NKJV)

3. One example of a prophecy in the Bible that came true is: A prophet said Israel's Messiah (a king expected to save them) would be born in the town <u>Bethlehem</u>. Jesus fulfilled this prophecy many years later when He was born in Bethlehem.

4. Amanda reads the <u>Bible</u> and goes to <u>church</u> to learn more about God.

## Chapter 4: Can Anyone Prove God Is Not Real?

1. What things do you know exist that you cannot see? Wind, gravity, love, anger, patience, joy, hope, and faith.

2. We know something exists that we can't see because we can see the <u>effect</u> of it. For example, even though we can't see wind, we can see wind <u>move</u> leaves on trees.

3. Millions of people had their lives changed through their <u>relationship</u> with God's Son, Jesus. Because of that, no one can prove God is not <u>real</u>.

4. Why do you think God doesn't appear in human form in front us right now to show us He exists? As we discover and learn about God, we grow in our heart, mind, and actions. God reveals to us what we are ready to understand through Jesus and the Bible. God and His ways are more than we can understand.

   "God's voice thunders in marvelous ways; he does great things beyond our understanding." (Job 37:5: NIV)

   "For you know that when your faith is tested, your endurance has a chance to grow. So let it grow, for when your endurance is fully developed, you will be perfect and complete, needing nothing. If you need wisdom, ask our generous God, and he will give it to you. He will not rebuke you for asking." (James 1:3-5 NLT)

## Chapter 5: How Has God Changed People?

1. People are more <u>content</u> with their lives when having a relationship with God.

   God wants us to live a full, meaningful life.

   "A thief comes only to steal and kill and destroy. I have come so they may have life. I want them to have it in the fullest possible way." (John 10:10 NIrV)

2. People still have <u>hard</u> <u>times</u> after becoming friends with God. But God promises to <u>help</u> us through our hard times.

   People still go through pain, loss, and sadness after they have a relationship with God. However, God helps us through it.

   "I have told you these things, so that you can have peace because of me. In this world you will have trouble. But be encouraged! I have won the battle over the world." (John 16:33 NIrV)

   "And we know that in all things God works for the good of those who love him, who have been called according to his purpose." (Romans 8:28 NIV)

   "I can do all things through Christ who strengthens me." (Phil 4:13 NKJV)

3. Other peoples' bad choices and sometimes our own bad choices cause us <u>pain</u>, not God.

   "Come to me, all you who are weary and burdened, and I will give you rest." (Matthew 11:28 NIV)

4.  Even though we can't see God, millions of people can feel the effect of God's <u>love</u> in their hearts, minds, and actions.

    "Whoever does not love does not know God, because God is love." (1 John 4:8 NIV)

5.  If you already have a relationship with God, how is your life different than before?

Before having a relationship with God (accepting Jesus Christ as Lord and Savior), many people focus mainly on benefiting themselves. They also carry guilt that resulted from their bad choices.

After having a relationship with God, many people

- learn to forgive themselves for bad choices they make because Jesus paid the price for our bad choices,
- focus more on understanding God and doing His will.
- learn to love themselves and others better as they understand God's love for them, and
- are comforted by knowing God loves them, wants the very best for them, and will use even our struggles (pain, sickness, and sadness) for good while helping them through it.
- understand that God created them for a special purpose, even though they made mistakes and will make mistakes again in the future.

Christians are the only people who can have hope in pain and suffering.

- Their lives become more fulfilling and meaningful.
- They work more at doing things the way God wants them to rather than doing things their own way.

- They receive peace with themselves, circumstances, and God's will, knowing the Holy Spirit lives in their hearts to guide and strengthen them.
- They have assurance that the pain and suffering are only temporary and that one day, God will separate them from all pain and suffering.

"But the Helper, the Holy Spirit, whom the Father will send in My name, He will teach you all things, and bring to your remembrance all things that I said to you." (John 14:26 NKJV)

"And we know that in all things God works for the good of those who love him, who have been called according to his purpose." (Romans 8:28 NIV)

"Praise be to the God and Father of our Lord Jesus Christ, the Father of compassion and the God of all comfort, who comforts us in all our troubles, so that we can comfort those in any trouble with the comfort we ourselves receive from God." (2 Corinthians 1:3–4 NIV)

6. A spiritual gift is a special <u>talent</u> God gives you after you become friends with Him, and begin a relationship with Him. God wants us to use our special talents to help others and serve God. Examples of spiritual gifts include leadership, teaching, encouragement, mercy, evangelism, discernment, wisdom, giving, and help.

"God has given each of you a gift from his great variety of spiritual gifts. Use them well to serve one another." (1 Peter 4:10 NLT)

7. What spiritual gift(s) do you think God gave you? Examples of spiritual gifts include leadership, teaching, encouragement, mercy, evangelism, discernment, wisdom, giving, and help.

There are free spiritual gift tests available on the Internet. God can also use other people to encourage us in areas where we are spiritually gifted.

> "Every good and perfect gift is from above, coming down from the Father of the heavenly lights, who does not change like shifting shadows." (James 1:17 NIV)

**Chapter 6: Who Is the Real God?**

1.  What does God look like? God is made of <u>three</u> distinct individuals: the <u>Father</u>, <u>the Son (Jesus)</u>, and the <u>Holy Spirit</u>.

We can't see God, but the Bible tells us there is one God in three distinct individuals: the Father, the Son, Jesus, and the Holy Spirit. Even though there are three individuals to God, there is just one God. Many children have trouble with God being made up of three distinct individuals. It may help to use this analogy: An egg has three parts, the egg shell, yolk, and white, even though the egg is just one egg.

# God Is Three Individuals

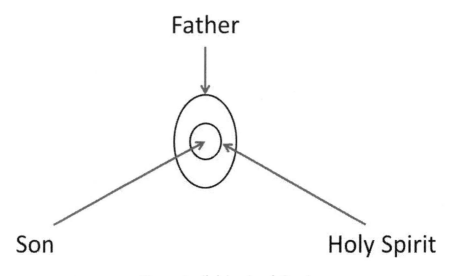

Three Individuals of God

Note about diagram: The egg displayed is purely for helping the reader overcome the obstacle to understanding God is one God even though God is Three Individuals. God is not like an egg. God's magnificence, power, love, accessibility and other qualities are much greater and complex than we can comprehend. The analogy of egg parts helped ease my confusion about the Trinity so I include it to help others with the same struggle.

> "Jesus answered, I am the way and the truth and the life. No one comes to the Father except through me." (John 14:6 NIV)

> "All that the Father gives Me will come to Me, and the one who comes to Me I will by no means cast out. For I have come down from heaven, not to do My own will, but the will of Him who sent Me." (John 6:37–38 NKJV)

> "God is spirit." (John 4:24a NKJV)

> "However, when He, the Spirit of truth, has come, He will guide you into all truth; for He will not speak on His own authority, but whatever He hears He will speak; and He will tell you things to come." (John 16:13 NKJV)

> "But the Helper, the Holy Spirit, whom the Father will send in My name, He will teach you all things, and bring to your remembrance all things that I said to you." (John 14:26 NKJV)

> Characteristics of God include perfect, eternal, gracious, faithful, kind, righteous, unique, truth, accessible, love, just, patient, good, forgiving, merciful, never changes, majestic.

> "God's way is perfect. All the LORD's promises prove true. He is a shield for all who look to him for protection." (Psalm 18:30 NLT)

> "I am the Alpha and the Omega—the beginning and the end," says the Lord God. "I am the one who is, who always was, and who is still to come—the Almighty One." (Revelation 1:8 NLT)

"But my life is worth nothing to me unless I use it for finishing the work assigned me by the Lord Jesus— the work of telling others the Good News about the wonderful grace of God." (Acts 20:24 NLT)

"God will do this, for he is faithful to do what he says, and he has invited you into partnership with his Son, Jesus Christ our Lord." (1 Corinthians 1:9 NLT)

"The LORD is gracious and righteous; our God is full of compassion." (Psalm 116:5 NIV)

"Whoever does not love does not know God, because God is love." (1 John 4:8 NIV)

"It is God who justifies." (Romans 8:33b NIV)

"The Lord is not slow in keeping his promise, as some understand slowness. Instead he is patient with you, not wanting anyone to perish, but everyone to come to repentance." (2 Peter 3:9 NIV)

"for it is God who works in you to will and to act in order to fulfill his good purpose." (Philippians 2:13 NIV)

"The Lord our God is merciful and forgiving, even though we have rebelled against him;" (Daniel 9:9 NIV)

"O Lord, God of Israel, you are just." (Ezra 9:15 NLT)

"Who among the gods is like you, LORD? Who is like you— majestic in holiness, awesome in glory, working wonders?" (Exodus 15:11 NIV)

"Whatever is good and perfect is a gift coming down to us from God our Father, who created all the lights in the heavens. He never changes or casts a shifting shadow." (James 1:17 NLT)

"For God is Spirit, so those who worship him must worship in spirit and in truth." (John 4:24 NLT)

2. What does each individual of God do? The Father created a plan for us to have a relationship with God. Jesus fulfilled the plan. The Holy Spirit guides us.

# Functions of 3 Individuals of God

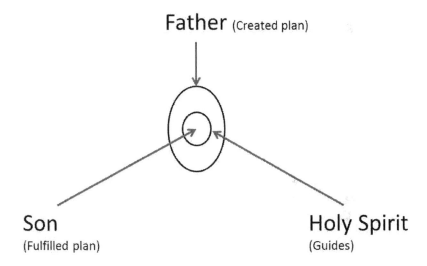

Functions of the Individuals of God

The Father defined the plan for humans to have a loving relationship with God.

The Son (Jesus) fulfilled the Father's plan of salvation for all mankind.

The Holy Spirit dwells within a person after he asks God to forgive his sins and be his Lord and Savior. The Holy Spirit also guides a person to make good choices and understand God's will.

The three Individuals of God are united in mind, purpose, and will and have the same goal.

Children may have trouble with the individuals of God having different functions, yet being one God; remind them that an egg is still one egg even though it has three different parts that have different functions. The egg shell protects. The egg yolk supplies food. The egg white keeps the yolk centered and supplies additional nutrients.

Unlike an egg, God never changes. He has always been there and always will. God is much more complex than we are, so it's okay to have questions about God and not fully understand Him.

Bible references explaining God include:

> "Jesus answered, I am the way and the truth and the life. No one comes to the Father except through me." (John 14:6 NIV)

> "But when the fullness of the time had come, God sent forth His Son, born of a woman, born under the law, to redeem those who were under the law, that we might receive the adoption as sons." (Galatians 4:4–5 NKJV)

> "All that the Father gives Me will come to Me, and the one who comes to Me I will by no means cast out. For I have come down from heaven, not to do My own will, but the will of Him who sent Me." (John 6:37–38 NKJV)

> "However, when He, the Spirit of truth, has come, He will guide you into all truth; for He will not speak on His own authority, but whatever He hears He will speak; and He will tell you things to come." (John 16:13 NKJV)

> "Now hope does not disappoint because the love of God has been poured out in our hearts by the Holy Spirit who was given to us." (Romans 5:5 NKJV)

"But the Helper, the Holy Spirit, whom the Father will send in My name, He will teach you all things, and bring to your remembrance all things that I said to you." (John 14:26 NKJV)

"But the Holy Spirit produces this kind of fruit in our lives: love, joy, peace, patience, kindness, goodness, faithfulness, gentleness, and self-control. There is no law against these things!" (Galatians 5:22–23 NLT)

"God is spirit." (John 4:24a NKJV)

"And you will seek Me [God] and find Me, when you search for Me with all your heart." (Jeremiah 29:13 NKJV)

"For God so loved the world that he gave his one and only Son, that whoever believes in him shall not perish but have eternal life. For God did not send His Son into the world to condemn the world, but to save the world through Him." (John 3:16-17 NIV)

"The Lord is not slow in keeping his promise, as some understand slowness. Instead he is patient with you, not wanting anyone to perish, but everyone to come to repentance." (2 Peter 3:9 NIV)

"Jesus Christ is the same yesterday, today, and forever." (Hebrews 13:8 NKJV)

"The Son is the exact likeness of God, who can't be seen. The Son is first, and he is over all creation. All things were created in him. He created everything in heaven and on earth. He created everything that can be seen and everything that can't be seen. He created kings, powers, rulers and authorities. All things have been created by him and for him. Before anything was created, he was already there. He holds everything together." (Colossians 1:15–17 NIrV)

"But God, who is rich in mercy, because of His great love with which He loved us." (Ephesians 2:4 NKJV)

"God is the only one who can't die. He lives in light that no one can get close to. No one has seen Him. Honor and power belong to Him forever. Amen." (1 Timothy 6:16 NIrV)

"Therefore go and make disciples of all nations, baptizing them in the name of the Father and of the Son and of the Holy Spirit." (Matthew 28:19 NIV)

"Now the earth was formless and empty, darkness was over the surface of the deep, and the Spirit of God was hovering over the waters." (Genesis 1:2 NIV)

"Your eyes are too pure to look at what is evil. You can't put up with the wrong things people do." (Habakkuk 1:13a NIrV)

"In the same way, the Spirit helps us in our weakness. We do not know what we ought to pray for, but the Spirit himself intercedes for us through wordless groans. And he who searches our hearts knows the mind of the Spirit, because the Spirit intercedes for God's people in accordance with the will of God." (Romans 8:26–27 NIV)

3. God never causes suffering because He is <u>perfect</u>. He is pure and completely separate from anything that is <u>impure</u>. God does allow us to go through hard times and helps us through our hard times.

   "God's way is perfect. The LORD's word doesn't have any flaws. He is like a shield to all who go to him for safety." (Psalm 18:30 NIrV)

Sin was not in God's original creation.

"God saw all that he had made, and it was very good."
(Genesis 1:31 NIV)

Satan tempted Eve (the first human woman) to sin, and Adam sinned with her by eating the forbidden fruit. This desire to sin is passed down from Adam and Eve to us. God allows sin so people can make their own choice about establishing a relationship with God.

4.  God is all-loving and never changes.

    "God is love." (1 John 4:8b NKJV)

    "I the LORD do not change. So you, the descendants of Jacob, are not destroyed." (Malachi 3:6 NIV)

## Chapter 7: Why Should I Be Friends with God?

1.  Amanda realized she sinned and her <u>sin</u> separates her from God. Have you ever disobeyed your parents or done something wrong even when you thought no one saw you?

The consequence of sin is eternal separation from God. Even though God loves everyone, our sin separates us from God, which prevents us from having any kind of relationship with Him.

> "For all have sinned and fall short of the glory of God." (Romans 3:23 NKJV)

> "They demonstrate that God's law is written in their hearts, for their own conscience and thoughts either accuse them or tell them they are doing right." (Romans 2:15 NLT)

2.  Sin separates us from God because God is <u>holy</u> (pure) and is completely separate from anything that is <u>impure</u>.

> "Your eyes are too pure to look at what is evil. You can't put up with the wrong things people do." (Habakkuk 1:13a NIrV)

3.  After we die physically our spirit will either live forever with God surrounded by love or separated from God in <u>hell</u>. Eternal separation from God is spiritual death.

Delaying your decision to be friends with God, so you can think about it, is just like rejecting God. You cannot change your mind about becoming friends with God after your physical body dies. Even though you may still have questions about God and feel there is much to be understood, you can still establish a relationship with God today.

"Anyone who is not with me is against me." (Matthew 12:30a NIrV)

"For the wages of sin is death, but the gift of God is eternal life in Christ Jesus our Lord." (Romans 6:23 NKJV)

"But God demonstrates His own love toward us, in that while we were still sinners, Christ died for us." (Romans 5:8 NKJV)

God is perfectly fair, loving, and just. Because Jesus never sinned, He was the only perfect way to pay the penalty for our sin. The good news is what Jesus did for us is a free gift. To receive this gift, each person must decide they want this free gift and establish a relationship with God.

Hell is eternal separation from God's love and is a horrible place.

In hell, "the worms that eat them do not die. The fire is not put out." (Mark 9:48 NIrV)

4. There is nothing we can do to make up for our <u>sin</u> and work our way to God.

Many people try to make up for the bad things they have done by going to church, being nice, giving money, or doing other nice things. However, doing these things does not take away anyone's sin nor remove the separation sin creates between you and God.

"If you confess with your mouth the Lord Jesus and believe in your heart that God has raised Him from the dead, you will be saved." (Romans 10:9 NKJV)

"The free gift of God's grace makes us right with him. Christ Jesus paid the price to set us free." (Romans 3:24)

5. Why do you think someone would not want to be friends with God?

- Some people have a hard time forgiving themselves, so they do not believe God or anyone else could forgive them.
- The guilt they carry from their bad choices can be overwhelming, and they do not feel they are lovable even though they are.
- People get deceived into believing they have to work their way to be friends with God, even though He knows we are unable to obey all of His commands, all the time. Only God is perfect.
- Some people prefer to delay their decision about becoming friends with God. Delaying your decision to be friends with God, so you can think about it, is just like rejecting God. If you die before you establish a relationship with God, there is no second chance.

"Are you jealous? Are you concerned only about getting ahead? Then your life will be a mess. You will be doing all kinds of evil things. But the wisdom that comes from heaven is pure. That's the most important thing about it. And that's not all. It also loves peace. It thinks about others. It obeys. It is full of mercy and good fruit. It is fair. It doesn't pretend to be what it is not." (James 3:16–17 NKJV)

6. If you are not friends with God, do you want to be friends with God now? If yes, be sure to guide them in saying the prayer in question 8-9 or something similar.

"Therefore, there is now no condemnation for those who are in Christ Jesus, because through Christ Jesus the law of the Spirit who gives life has set you free from the law of sin and death. For what the law was powerless to do because it was weakened by the flesh, God did by sending his own Son in the likeness of sinful flesh to be a sin offering. And so he condemned sin in the flesh, in order that the righteous requirement of the law might be fully met in us, who do not live according to the flesh but according to the Spirit.

Those who live according to the flesh have their minds set on what the flesh desires; but those who live in accordance with the Spirit have their minds set on what the Spirit desires. The mind governed by the flesh is death, but the mind governed by the Spirit is life and peace. The mind governed by the flesh is hostile to God; it does not submit to God's law, nor can it do so. Those who are in the realm of the flesh cannot please God." (Romans 8:1-8 NIV)

"'I know the plans I have for you,' announces the LORD. 'I want you to enjoy success. I do not plan to harm you. I will give you hope for the years to come." (Jeremiah 29:11 NIrV)

No one has an excuse to not know God. He makes His existence clear to everyone.

"For ever since the world was created, people have seen the earth and sky. Through everything God made, they can clearly see his invisible qualities—his eternal power and divine nature. So they have no excuse for not knowing God." (Romans 1:20 NIV)

"Yet you desired faithfulness even in the womb; you taught me wisdom in that secret place." (Psalm 51:6 NIV)

"Wealth is worthless in the day of wrath, but righteousness delivers from death." (Proverbs 11:4 NIV)

## Chapter 8: How Can I Be Friends with God?

1. Is there a sin barrier between you and God? There is a sin barrier if you ever broke any of God's commandments.

Every human being has broken at least one of God's commandments, so we all need to receive God's gift, Jesus, and establish a relationship with Him.

> "For all have sinned and fall short of the glory of God." (Romans 3:23 NKJV)

2. The penalty for sin is <u>spiritual</u> <u>death</u> which is eternal separation from God.

> "For the wages of sin is death, but the gift of God is eternal life in Christ Jesus our Lord." (Romans 6:23 NKJV)

> "You, however, are not in the realm of the flesh but are in the realm of the Spirit, if indeed the Spirit of God lives in you. And if anyone does not have the Spirit of Christ, they do not belong to Christ. But if Christ is in you, then even though your body is subject to death because of sin, the Spirit gives life because of righteousness. And if the Spirit of him who raised Jesus from the dead is living in you, he who raised Christ from the dead will also give life to your mortal bodies because of his Spirit who lives in you." (Romans 9-11 NIV)

3. God sent his Son, <u>Jesus Christ</u>, to help communicate His Love to us, pay the penalty for our sin, and make the way for us to have a relationship with Him.

> "God so loved the world that he gave his one and only Son. Anyone who believes in him will not die but will have eternal life." (John 3:16 NIRV)

"For God presented Jesus as the sacrifice for sin. People are made right with God when they believe that Jesus sacrificed his life, shedding his blood. This sacrifice shows that God was being fair when He held back and did not punish those who sinned in times past, for He was looking ahead and including them in what He would do in this present time. God did this to demonstrate his righteousness, for He himself is fair and just, and He makes sinners right in his sight when they believe in Jesus." (Romans 3:25–26 NLT)

"But God demonstrates His own love toward us, in that while we were still sinners, Christ died for us." (Romans 5:8 NKJV)

4. We can have a <u>relationship</u> ("be friends") with God after we overcome the sin barrier between us and <u>God</u> by believing what Jesus did for us and asking for forgiveness. This requires a genuine acceptance of what God did for us and a desire to obey God (change our heart).

"Jesus answered, "I am the way and the truth and the life. No one comes to the Father except through me." (John 14:6 NIV)

"For God presented Jesus as the sacrifice for sin. People are made right with God when they believe that Jesus sacrificed his life, shedding his blood. This sacrifice shows that God was being fair when He held back and did not punish those who sinned in times past, for He was looking ahead and including them in what He would do in this present time. God did this to demonstrate his righteousness, for He himself is fair and just, and He makes sinners right in his sight when they believe in Jesus." (Romans 3:25–26 NLT)

5. To overcome the sin barrier between yourself and God, you can pray the following prayer (or something similar): "Dear God, I'm sorry for my sins. Please forgive me. I believe Jesus paid the penalty for my sins and rose again. Please be my Savior, Lord, and Friend."

This decision to establish a relationship with God is the biggest decision of your life because it affects you for eternity. Asking God to be your Savior means believing Jesus died on the cross to save you from being separated from God forever. Asking God to be your Lord indicates you recognize God as your Creator and moral Leader and indicates you recognize God to be the primary One who guides you in determining what right from wrong. Asking God to be your Friend indicates you want a relationship with God and you desire to spend time with Him, trust Him, learn more about Him, and love Him.

"If you confess with your mouth the Lord Jesus and believe in your heart that God has raised Him from the dead, you will be saved." (Romans 10:9 NKJV)

"Through faith in Jesus we have received God's grace. In that grace we stand. We are full of joy because we expect to share in God's glory." (Romans 5:2 NIrV)

"For it is by grace you have been saved, through faith—and this is not from yourselves, it is the gift of God— not by works, so that no one can boast. For we are God's handiwork, created in Christ Jesus to do good works, which God prepared in advance for us to do." (Ephesians 2:8-10 NIV)

6. After you accept God's gift, Jesus, and ask for forgiveness for your sins, God places the Holy Spirit in you to help guide you to make good choices.

"There is therefore now no condemnation to those who are in Christ Jesus, who do not walk according to the flesh, but according to the Spirit." (Romans 8:1 NKJV)

You will still have hard times after you establish a relationship with God.

"Praise be to the God and Father of our Lord Jesus Christ, the Father of compassion and the God of all comfort, who comforts us in all our troubles, so that we can comfort those in any trouble with the comfort we ourselves receive from God. For just as we share abundantly in the sufferings of Christ, so also our comfort abounds through Christ. If we are distressed, it is for your comfort and salvation; if we are comforted, it is for your comfort, which produces in you patient endurance of the same sufferings we suffer. And our hope for you is firm, because we know that just as you share in our sufferings, so also you share in our comfort." (2 Corinthians 1:3–7 NIV)

In his book, *God Has A Wonderful Plan For Your Life*, Ray Comfort states, "Peace and joy are legitimate fruits of salvation, but it is not legitimate to use these fruits as a drawing card for salvation. If we do, the sinner will respond with an impure motive, lacking repentance."

7. Is it okay to sin after you become friends with God? No. Why not?

God wants you to do your best not to sin. We show God we love Him by obeying Him. The Holy Spirit will help make you more sensitive to sin and its negative impact. If you do sin, you will still have consequences but God will forgive you. Your spiritual body just won't be separated from God after your physical body dies. True repentance means you change your bad behavior and are sorry. Having an attitude of thinking it is okay to sin because it's covered under Christ's sacrifice reveals a lack of real repentance.

> "Jesus replied, 'Anyone who loves me will obey my teaching. My Father will love them. We will come to them and make our home with them.'" (John 14:23 NIrV)

> "For those who are led by the Spirit of God are the children of God." (Romans 8:14 NIV)

8. After you have a relationship with God, if you realize you sin, immediately ask God to <u>forgive</u> you and <u>change</u> your behavior to obey God.

> "Anyone who hides their sins doesn't succeed. But anyone who admits their sins and gives them up finds mercy." (Proverbs 28:13 NIrV)

> "If we say we have no sin, we deceive ourselves, and the truth is not in us. If we confess our sins, He is faithful and just to forgive us our sins and to cleanse us from all unrighteousness." (1 John 1:8–9 NKJV)

9. Do you want to establish a relationship ("be friends") with God? If yes, you can pray the following prayer (or something similar): "Dear God, I'm sorry for my sin. Please forgive me. I believe Jesus paid the penalty for my sin and rose again. Please be my Savior, Lord, and Friend."

This decision to establish a relationship with God is the biggest decision of your life because it affects you for eternity. Asking God to be your Savior means believing Jesus died on the cross to save you from being separated from God forever. Asking God to be your Lord indicates you recognize God as your Creator and moral Leader and indicates you recognize God to be the primary One who guides you in determining what right from wrong. Asking God to be your Friend indicates you want a relationship with God and you desire to spend time with Him, trust Him, learn more about Him, and love Him.

10. How is being "friends" with God different from being friends with people you know?

Our friends on earth sometimes make bad choices and hurt us. God is perfect and will never mislead you. God is more than a friend. He is your Spiritual Father and Creator of the entire universe. God understands everything about you, including the mistakes you will make in the future. He even knows the number of hairs on your head. He loves you more than you can imagine and wants you to freely choose to love Him. God's love is unconditional. He knows your mistakes and weaknesses and loves you despite what you have done in the past or will do in the future. He wants you to show your love for Him by obeying Him and allowing Him to use you as an instrument of His love in helping others. After you ask God to forgive your sins and accept Jesus as your Lord and Savior, nothing can ever separate you from God's love.

Our earthly friends cannot save us from the punishment of sin, but God sent His Son, Jesus to take the punishment for us. Jesus is our Savior, in addition to our friend, as long as we admit our sins, ask God to forgive our sins, and ask God to guide us in living our lives for Him.

> "But here is how God has shown his love for us. While we were still sinners, Christ died for us." (Romans 5:8 NIrV)

> "For I know the thoughts that I think toward you, says the LORD, thoughts of peace and not of evil, to give you a future and a hope." (Jeremiah 29:11 NKJV)

"Jesus replied, 'Anyone who loves me will obey my teaching. My Father will love them. We will come to them and make our home with them.'" (John 14:23 NIrV)

"For it is by grace you have been saved, through faith—and this is not from yourselves, it is the gift of God—not by works, so that no one can boast. For we are God's handiwork, created in Christ Jesus to do good works, which God prepared in advance for us to do." (Ephesians 2:8–10 NIV)

"We know what love is because Jesus Christ gave his life for us. So we should give our lives for our brothers and sisters…. God has commanded us to believe in the name of His Son, Jesus Christ. He has also commanded us to love one another. The one who obeys God's commands remains joined to Him. And He remains joined to them. Here is how we know that God lives in us. We know it because of the Holy Spirit He gave us." (1 John 3:16, 23–24 NIrV)

"Give praise to the God and Father of our Lord Jesus Christ. In his great mercy he has given us a new birth and a living hope. This hope is living because Jesus Christ rose from the dead. He has given us new birth so that we might share in what belongs to him. This is a gift that can never be destroyed. It can never spoil or even fade away. It is kept in heaven for you. Through faith you are kept safe by God's power. Your salvation is going to be completed. It is ready to be shown to you in the last days. Because you know all this, you have great joy. You have joy even though you may have had to suffer for a little while. You may have had to suffer sadness in all kinds of trouble. Your troubles have come in order to prove that your faith is real. Your faith is worth more than gold. That's because gold can pass away even when fire has made it pure. Your faith is meant to bring praise, honor, and glory to God. This will happen when Jesus Christ returns. Even though you have not seen him, you love him. Though you do not see him now, you believe in him. You are filled with a glorious joy that can't be put into words. You are receiving the salvation of your souls. This salvation is the final result of your faith." (1 Peter 1:3–9 NIrV)

"No one has greater love than the one who gives their life for their friends." (John 15:13 NIrV)

"Then Jesus cried out, 'Whoever believes in me does not believe in me only, but in the one who sent me. The one who looks at me is seeing the one who sent me. I have come into the world as a light, so that no one who believes in me should stay in darkness. If anyone hears my words but does not keep them, I do not judge that person. For I did not come to judge the world, but to save the world. There is a judge for the one who rejects me and does not accept my words; the very words I have spoken will condemn them at the last day. For I did not speak on my own, but the Father who sent me commanded me to say all that I have spoken. I know that his command leads to eternal life. So whatever I say is just what the Father has told me to say.'" (John 12:44–50 NIV)

"If you love me, keep my commands. And I will ask the Father, and he will give you another advocate to help you and be with you forever—the Spirit of truth. The world cannot accept him, because it neither sees him nor knows him. But you know him, for he lives with you and will be in you. I will not leave you as orphans; I will come to you. Before long, the world will not see me anymore, but you will see me. Because I live, you also will live." (John 14:15–19 NIV)

11. God created us so we can freely choose to establish a <u>relationship</u> with Him. The Bible tells us God gives everyone evidence of His existence so there is no excuse not to establish a relationship with Him.

Love is meaningful only if a person freely chooses to love. Because God gave us free choice, we can't make ourselves be perfectly obedient to God all of the time. We have a strong desire to do things our own way, which sometimes causes us to disobey God. Therefore, we need a Savior, Jesus. It is our choice to accept the gift of Jesus. To accept the gift of Jesus, we need to acknowledge that we believe God, the Father, sent His Son to pay the penalty for our sins, rose again, and also ask God to be our Lord and Savior. Doing this requires a change of heart and desire to love and be obedient to God. God is loving and patient with you as you slowly change and become more loving like Jesus.

> "They know the truth about God because he has made it obvious to them. For ever since the world was created, people have seen the earth and sky. Through everything God made, they can clearly see his invisible qualities—his eternal power and divine nature. So they have no excuse for not knowing God." (Romans 1:19–20 NLT)

> "For the wrath of God is revealed from heaven against all ungodliness and unrighteousness of men, who suppress the truth in unrighteousness, because what may be known of God is manifest in them, for God has shown *it* to them. For since the creation of the world His invisible *attributes* are clearly seen, being understood by the things that are made, *even* His eternal power and Godhead, so that they are without excuse." (Romans 1:18–19 NKJV)

**Chapter 9: What Should I Do after I Become Friends with God?**

1. After you establish a relationship with God, how can you grow closer to Him?

   - Pray and ask God to help you. God knows what you're feeling but loves it when you talk to Him and express your feelings. You can talk to God anywhere, anytime, about anything, just like a friend. Also, take time to listen to what God is saying back to you through the Holy Spirit in your heart. God sometimes speaks to you with a gentle nudge or a quiet whisper. Sometimes we just need to be silent and listen.
   - Attend a church that teaches you about the Bible. It will be fun as you encourage and serve each other. No church is perfect. In fact, every church is filled with people who openly admit they are not perfect and need God in their lives to help them learn and live a fulfilling life.
   - Get baptized. This is an outward sign to show others your decision to establish a relationship with God and He wants every person to get baptized.
   - Read the Bible and join a youth group or Sunday school class. Obeying God is a true sign of your love for God and the only way you can know if you are obeying God is to know His word. Ask for a Bible from a church near you or your parents. You can also read the Bible on the Internet website, Bible Gateway. Bible versions that are easier to read for kids include New International Readers Version (NIrV) and New King James Version (NKJV). I recommend starting with the book of John.
   - Help others. After you are convinced that God is real and that Jesus died on the cross to save you from your sins, ask Jesus to be your Lord and Savior. God will give you spiritual gifts. To find out what

gift God gave you, take a spiritual gift test. There are several spiritual gift tests on the Internet; an excellent book is *Discover Your Children's Gifts*, by Don and Katie Fortune. Once you discover your gift, you can use it to help others and the church. As you allow God to use you, He will stretch you and bless you in ways you never imagined.

• Continue to keep your heart clean by regularly telling God your sins. It's not enough to simply talk to God about your sins and say you're sorry. You also need to change your bad behavior.

Supporting Scripture for this question is grouped by listed action that one can take to further develop their relationship with God (Pray, Attend Church, Get Baptized, Read the Bible, and Help Others).

### Pray:

"Always be joyful. Never stop praying. Be thankful in all circumstances, for this is God's will for you who belong to Christ Jesus." (1 Thessalonians 5:16-18 NLT)

"Then you will call on me and come and pray to me, and I will listen to you. You will seek me and find me when you seek me with all your heart." (Jeremiah 29:12-13 NIV)

"The LORD detests the sacrifice of the wicked, but the prayer of the upright pleases him." (Proverbs 15:8 NIV)

"If we claim we have no sin, we are only fooling ourselves and not living in the truth. But if we confess our sins to him, he is faithful and just to forgive us our sins and to cleanse us from all wickedness." (1 John 1:8-9 NLT)

**Attend Church:**
"And let us consider how we may spur one another on toward love and good deeds, not giving up meeting together, as some are in the habit of doing, but encouraging one another—and all the more as you see the Day approaching." (Hebrews 10:25 NIV)

"so in Christ we, though many, form one body, and each member belongs to all the others." (Romans 12:5 NIV)

"Their responsibility is to equip God's people to do his work and build up the church, the body of Christ. This will continue until we all come to such unity in our faith and knowledge of God's Son that we will be mature in the Lord, measuring up to the full and complete standard of Christ.

Then we will no longer be immature like children. We won't be tossed and blown about by every wind of new teaching. We will not be influenced when people try to trick us with lies so clever they sound like the truth. Instead, we will speak the truth in love, growing in every way more and more like Christ, who is the head of his body, the church. He makes the whole body fit together perfectly. As each part does its own special work, it helps the other parts grow, so that the whole body is healthy and growing and full of love." (Ephesians 4:12-16 NLT)

**Get Baptized:**
"Therefore go and make disciples of all nations, baptizing them in the name of the Father and of the Son and of the Holy Spirit, and teaching them to obey everything I have commanded you. And surely I am with you always, to the very end of the age." (Matthew 28:19-20 NIV)

"We were therefore buried with him through baptism into death in order that, just as Christ was raised from the dead through the glory of the Father, we too may live a new life.

For if we have been united with him in a death like his, we will certainly also be united with him in a resurrection like his. For we know that our old self was crucified with him so that the body ruled by sin might be done away with, that we should no longer be slaves to sin— because anyone who has died has been set free from sin.

Now if we died with Christ, we believe that we will also live with him. For we know that since Christ was raised from the dead, he cannot die again; death no longer has mastery over him. The death he died, he died to sin once for all; but the life he lives, he lives to God.

In the same way, count yourselves dead to sin but alive to God in Christ Jesus. Therefore do not let sin reign in your mortal body so that you obey its evil desires. Do not offer any part of yourself to sin as an instrument of wickedness, but rather offer yourselves to God as those who have been brought from death to life; and offer every part of yourself to him as an instrument of righteousness. For sin shall no longer be your master, because you are not under the law, but under grace." (Romans 6:4-14 NIV)

**Read the Bible:**
"All Scripture is inspired by God and is useful to teach us what is true and to make us realize what is wrong in our lives. It corrects us when we are wrong and teaches us to do what is right. God uses it to prepare and equip his people to do every good work." (2 Timothy 3:16-17 NLT)

"Jesus replied, You are in error because you do not know the Scriptures or the power of God." (Matthew 22:29 NIV)

"Your word is like a lamp that shows me the way. It is like a light that guides me." (Psalm 119:105 NIrV)

"Every word of God is perfect. He is like a shield to those who trust in him. He keeps them safe." (Proverbs 30:5 NIrV)

**Help Others:**
"Carry one another's heavy loads. If you do, you will fulfill the law of Christ." (Galatians 6:2 NIrV)

"Therefore, I urge you, brothers and sisters, in view of God's mercy, to offer your bodies as a living sacrifice, holy and pleasing to God—this is your true and proper worship. Do not conform to the pattern of this world, but be transformed by the renewing of your mind. Then you will be able to test and approve what God's will is—his good, pleasing and perfect will." (Romans 12:1-2 NIV)

"Suppose a person claims to have faith but doesn't act on their faith. My brothers and sisters, can this kind of faith save them? Suppose a brother or a sister has no clothes or food. Suppose one of you says to them, "Go. I hope everything turns out fine for you. Keep warm. Eat well." And suppose you do nothing about what they really need. Then what good have you done? It is the same with faith. If it doesn't cause us to do something, it's dead." (James 2:14-17 NIrV)

"In the same way, let your good deeds shine out for all to see, so that everyone will praise your heavenly Father." (Matthew 5:16 NLT)

"If you help the poor, you are lending to the LORD—and he will repay you!" (Proverbs 19:17 NLT)

"Just as our bodies have many parts and each part has a special function, so it is with Christ's body. We are many parts of one body, and we all belong to each other.

In his grace, God has given us different gifts for doing certain things well. So if God has given you the ability to prophesy, speak out with as much faith as God has given you. If your gift is serving others, serve them well. If you are a teacher, teach well. If your gift is to encourage others, be encouraging. If it is giving, give generously. If God has given you leadership ability, take the responsibility seriously. And if you have a gift for showing kindness to others, do it gladly." (Romans 12:4-8 NLT)

"God's gifts of grace come in many forms. Each of you has received a gift in order to serve others. You should use it faithfully. If anyone speaks, they should do it as one speaking God's words. If anyone serves, they should do it with the strength God provides. Then in all things God will be praised through Jesus Christ. Glory and power belong to him for ever and ever. Amen." (1 Peter 4:10-11 NIrV)

2.  Why is it important to know why you believe in God?

So you can answer someone else's questions about God and then they too can accept God's gift, Jesus, and establish a relationship with Him. In the Bible, God tells us to always be prepared to give the reason for your hope.

"But make sure that in your hearts you honor Christ as Lord. Always be ready to give an answer to anyone who asks you about the hope you have. Be ready to give the reason for it. But do it gently and with respect." (1 Peter 3:15 NIrV)

If you have comments or recommendations for additional questions, please send them to IsGodRealKids@gmail.com.

# References

**Printed Material**

Comfort, Ray. *God Has a Wonderful Plan for Your Life. The Myth of the Modern Message.* Bellflower, CA: Living Waters Publications, 2010.

Comfort, Ray. *Scientific Facts in the Bible: 100 Reasons to Believe the Bible Is Supernatural in Origin.* Alachua, FL: Bridge-Logos Publishers, 2001.

Fortune, Don, and Katie Fortune. *Discover Your Children's Gifts.* Grand Rapids, MI: Chosen Books, 1989.

Glueck, Nelson. *Rivers in the Desert: A History of the Negev.* New York: Farrar, Straus and Cudahy, 1959.

Ham, Ken, and Cindy Malott. *The Answers Book for Kids Vol. 3.* 2009.

Hodge, Bodie, Tommy Mitchell, and Ken Ham. *The Answers Book 4 Teens Vol 1: Your Questions, God's Answers,* 2011.

Little, Paul. *Know Why You Believe.* Downers Grove, IL: InterVarsity Press, 2008.

McDowell, Josh. *The New Evidence that Demands a Verdict.* Nashville, TN: Thomas Nelson, 1999.

McDowell, Josh, and Bill Wilson. *Evidence for the Historical Jesus: A Compelling Case for His Life and His Claims.* Eugene, OR: Harvest House Publishers, 1988.

McDowell, Josh, and Kevin Johnson. *The Awesome Book of Bible Answers for Kids.* Eugene, OR: Harvest House Publishers, 2003.

McDowell, Josh, and Sean McDowell. *The Unshakable Truth: How You Can Experience the 12 Essentials of a Relevant Faith.* Eugene, OR: Harvest House Publishers, 2010.

Seed, Hal, and Dan Grider. *The God Questions*. Colorado Springs, CO: Outreach Publishing. 2007.

Strobel, Lee. *Case for Faith for Kids*. Grand Rapids, MI: Zonderkidz, 2010.


## Websites

Bible Gateway (n.d.). www.biblegateway.com.

Christianity Today (2018). www.christianitytoday.com.

Creation Network. (2018). www.creationnetwork.org.

Focus on the Family (1997–2018). www.focusonthefamily.com.

Got Questions Ministries (2002-2018). www.gotquestions.org.

Hovind, Eric (2018). Creation Today. www.creationtoday.org.

Institute for Creation Research (2018). www.icr.org.

Kids of Integrity (2018). www.kidsofintegrity.com.

Lewis, C.S. (2018). Apologetics: C.S. Lewis Society of Intelligent Faith. www.apologetics.org.

Merriam-Webster (2018). www.merriam-webster.com.

# Endnotes

### Chapter 2: How Can You Create Something Out of Nothing?
1. McDowell, Josh, and Sean McDowell. *The Unshakable Truth: How You Can Experience the 12 Essentials of a Relevant Faith.* Eugene, OR: Harvest House Publishers, 2010, 93.

### Glossary
Merriam-Webster Dictionary at http://www.merriam-webster.com/dictionary.

### Discussion Question Answers
1. Comfort, Ray. *God Has a Wonderful Plan for Your Life. The Myth of the Modern Message.* Bellflower, CA: Living Waters Publications, 2010.

# Reflections

Reflection for chapter 1: Were you ever ashamed to admit you believe in God? If yes, why? If not, why not?

_____

_____

_____

_____

_____

_____

_____

_____

_____

_____

_____

_____

_____

_____

_____

_____

_____

_____

_____

_____

_____

_____

_____

_____

_____

_____

_____

_____

Reflection for chapter 2: What convinces you God created our world?

_____

_____

_____

_____

_____

_____

_____

_____

_____

_____

_____

_____

_____

_____

_____

_____

_____

_____

_____

_____

_____

_____

_____

_____

_____

_____

_____

_____

_____

_____

_____

_____

# Reflection for chapter 3: Why do you believe the Bible?

Reflection for chapter 4: Why can't faith be based on feelings alone? When have you struggled with doubt and what was the outcome?

_____
_____
_____
_____
_____
_____
_____
_____
_____
_____
_____
_____
_____
_____
_____
_____
_____
_____
_____
_____
_____
_____
_____
_____
_____
_____
_____
_____
_____
_____
_____
_____

Reflection for chapter 5: Describe your life before you established a relationship with God? How has your life changed after you established a relationship with God?

_____
_____
_____
_____
_____
_____
_____
_____
_____
_____
_____
_____
_____
_____
_____
_____
_____
_____
_____
_____
_____
_____
_____
_____
_____
_____
_____
_____

Reflection for chapter 6: How would you describe God? What convinces you God is real?

_____
_____
_____
_____
_____
_____
_____
_____
_____
_____
_____
_____
_____
_____
_____
_____
_____
_____
_____
_____
_____
_____
_____
_____
_____
_____
_____
_____
_____
_____
_____
_____

Reflection for chapter 7: Some people think they're okay with God because they consider their sins not as bad as others. What do you think of that?

_____
_____
_____
_____
_____
_____
_____
_____
_____
_____
_____
_____
_____
_____
_____
_____
_____
_____
_____
_____
_____
_____
_____
_____
_____
_____
_____
_____
_____
_____

Reflection for chapter 8: How is being in a relationship with God different than being friends with people you know?

_____

_____

_____

_____

_____

_____

_____

_____

_____

_____

_____

_____

_____

_____

_____

_____

_____

_____

_____

_____

_____

_____

_____

_____

_____

_____

_____

_____

_____

_____

_____

Reflection for chapter 9: How will you show Jesus you are grateful for what He did?

Made in United States
Orlando, FL
01 September 2023

36626610R00080